Forgotten Lives

Exploring the History of Learning Disability

by
Dorothy Atkinson
Mark Jackson
Jan Walmsley

British Library Cataloguing in Publication Data

A CIP record for this book is available from the British Library

ISBN 1 873791 84 4

© Copyright 1997 BILD Publications

BILD Publications is the publishing office of the
British Institute of Learning Disabilities
Wolverhampton Road
Kidderminster
Worcestershire
United Kingdom
DY10 3PP.
Telephone: 01562 850251
Fax: 01562 851970
e-mail bild@bild.demon.co,uk.

BILD Publications are distributed worldwide by
Plymbridge Distributors Limited
Estover House
Plymouth
United Kingdom
PL6 7PZ
Telephone: 01752 202300
Fax: 01752 202333.

Printed by The Cookley Printers Limited
56 Bridge Road
Cookley
Kidderminster
Worcestershire
United Kingdom
DY10 3SB.

Contents

List of Contributors

Dorothy Atkinson is a Senior Lecturer in the School of Health and Social Welfare at the Open University. Her background is in social work, and includes several years' experience of working with people with learning disabilities. Her OU work has included co-editing the anthology *'Know Me As I Am'*. Her current interest is in exploring the use of auto/biographical research with people with learning disabilities in order to enable individuals and groups to tell their stories.

Mabel Cooper is an active member of the self-advocacy movement. She was chairperson of People First, London for two years (1994-96) and then vice-chair. She is currently a member of the London branch and is also a member of People First, Croydon. Her self-advocacy activities have included speaking at conferences, running workshops and representing People First on national and international bodies.

Rebecca Fido is currently an Assistant Psychologist at the Learning Disability Services for Leeds Community and Mental Health Services NHS Trust undertaking clinical work and research responsibilities. These include co-editing a booklet on issues involved in resettling people with severe and profound disabilities into the community. She had previously worked as an assistant psychologist (with Maggie Potts), a research associate and a further education tutor for students with learning disabilities.

Richard Harris, M.A., is the Assistant County Archivist at the Essex Record Office. He was responsible for the collection, selection and deposit of the records of South Ockendon Hospital at the county record office.

Mark Jackson is a Research Fellow and Lecturer in the Wellcome Unit for the History of Medicine at the University of Manchester. His published works include *New-born child murder: women, illegitimacy and the courts in eighteenth-century England*, (Manchester University Press, 1996), and numerous articles on the history of infanticide and the history of mental deficiency. Originally trained as an immunologist and medical practitioner, he is currently developing a research project on the history of asthma.

Maggie Potts is a Manager of Clinical Psychology, Psychotherapy and Counselling Services for the Leeds Community and Mental Health

NHS Trust. She is a Consultant Clinical Psychologist who has worked therapeutically for many years with people who have learning disabilities. She has a long standing research interest in the effects of resettlement from institutions into ordinary housing in the community, and, with Rebecca Fido, edited a history of a hospital for people with learning disabilities based on the reminiscences of some of its older residents. This was published under the title 'A Fit Person to be Removed' (Northcote House, 1991).

Julia Sheppard BA, Dip Arch Admin, has been Archivist of the Contemporary Medical Archives Centre since it was established at the Wellcome Institute for the History of Medicine in 1979. She is co-editor of *British Archives: A Guide to Archive Resources in the UK* (Macmillan, 3rd ed. 1995).

Andrew Stevens is Divisional Head for Learning Difficulties at the Anglia Polytechnic University. He was previously employed by the Central Council for Education and Training in Social Work after a career in social work in North East Essex. He is currently completing his doctoral dissertation on the Royal Eastern Counties Institution and has published a number of articles on social work, disability and community care.

Jan Walmsley is a Senior Lecturer in the School of Health and Social Welfare at the Open University. Her first degree was in history and she has brought this interest in the past to bear on a more recent area of interest, learning disability. Her PhD thesis, *Gender, Caring and Learning Disability* 1994 gave her the opportunity to begin to research the history of community care for people with learning difficulties and she continues to see this as her main focus of interest.

Acknowledgements

The preparation of this book has been a collaborative venture, and has involved many people at various stages in its development. The editors wish to acknowledge the contributions of all those who have helped to bring this volume into being, and to thank the organisations, groups and individuals who have played a key role in the process.

The editors wish to thank the Open University's School of Health and Social Welfare, the National Development Team and the Wellcome Trust for their overall support of our research into the history of learning disability. Thanks are due especially to the OU and the NDT for their joint sponsorship of the seminar on the Social History of Learning Disability which was held at the Open University in July 1994. The papers presented at that seminar form the basis of the chapters in this book. We are grateful to everyone who contributed to the seminar and to those people who went on to prepare their papers as chapters.

We also want to express our personal thanks to John Harris at BILD for his help and advice in preparing the manuscript for publication. We want to say a warm 'thank you' to Yvonne Aspinall for preparing some chapters in draft, and to Christine Finch and Janet Vango for their careful typing, layout and presentation of the manuscript at all stages.

Special thanks are due to people who have advised and supported us at various stages and in various ways. We are especially grateful to Paul Taylor whose enthusiasm for the project, the seminar and the book has remained undiminished - and who has contributed a personal foreword to the book. Thanks are due also to Mathew Thomson, for his advice on the script; to John Pickstone, from the Wellcome Unit for the History of Medicine in Manchester, for first pointing out the wealth of archival records from Sandlebridge; and to Michelle Garret at People First, for her support of Mabel Cooper. Finally, we have some personal thanks for our friends and families who have supported us throughout. Thank you to Peter Sharpe; Siobhan, Ciara and Riordan; to James and Katie Walmsley and Jane Read.

Photographs and Illustrations

Grateful acknowledgement is made to the following sources for permission to reproduce the photographs and illustrations in this book:

pp.23, 25: Lifecare NHS Trust, Caterham; pp.40, 44: Community and Mental Health Services Trust (anon); pp.59, 60: Andy Stevens, Anglia Polytechnic University; Figure 5.1: from the Annual Report of the Lancashire and Cheshire Society for the Permanent Care of the Feeble-Minded, 1910, facing p.10; Figure 5.2: Annual Report, as above, 1905, facing p.10; Figure 5.3: Annual Report, as above, 1903, facing p.5; Figure 5.4: Annual Report, as above, 1910, facing p.15; p.77: Local Studies Library, London Borough of Newham; p.78: Randal Bingley, Essex, private collection; p.85: Susan and Robert Howard, the Local History Press; p.110: Frome Museum collection; p.118: Fred Davis, Shepton Mallet; p.130: courtesy of the Wellcome Institute Library, ref. V0000000B00/V30034 (Shuttleworth Collection, Western MSS Department); p.132: courtesy of the Wellcome Institute Library, ref. CMAC/SA/Q1/454 (Chartered Society of Physiotherapy). Front cover: pictures from Lapage C. P. (1911) *Feeblemindedness in Children of School-Age*, Manchester University Press.

Cover design: The Rural Media Company.

Foreword

It is nearly six years since I met with Frances Brown and Derek Thomas, both of the National Development Team for People with Learning Disabilities, to discuss a strange absence which concerned us all. In all the work being done, in all the money being spent on the shift from institutional to community-based services for people with learning disabilities, there was no real sense of history. Charred scraps of paper, containing clues to the reality of the lives of thousands, were dancing over the bonfires of closing institutions. No records were being kept, no photographs of the wards, no biographies of the people, not even a home video of the bonfire. And away from institutions, families, friends and paid workers were building some kind of alternative in the communities, usually unrewarded and always unrecorded. In our work in teaching paid staff in community settings, we noticed over and over again that they had very little awareness of what life had been like for disabled people in the earlier decades of this century, and only a limited understanding of the reasons for change. The books concerned with these issues could be counted on the fingers of one hand. Collectively, we seemed determined to eliminate the past and leave no trace of the present.

And yet we knew from our connections with disabled people and their families that there were many and important accounts of endurance, tenacity, loss, generosity, injustice and triumph waiting to be told, and thousands of willing story-tellers. Still there was no one place for their voices to be heard and no way to amplify those voices to the benefit of us all. Clearly, what was needed was an initiative to collect and publicise the recent history of people with learning disabilities, both in and out of the institutions which have been so much a feature of this century's response to those people. There was a need for a visual, documentary and oral history to be seized while there were still images for film to record, still papers to be analysed and catalogued, and still breath to reveal those forgotten lives. We set up a small project, on a shoestring, to find out what was available, make contacts, and invite contributions. We soon discovered that the task was far too great for our slender means, but that a lot of other people had had the same thoughts.

The problem was that this was nobody's business. Everyone we spoke to (Local Authorities, NHS Trusts, Government Departments, Universities, Charitable Trusts) agreed that this was important and essential work which someone (else) ought to be doing. In the end, the only people who were able to give the task the necessary priority were a small number of academic historians and the School of Health and

Social Welfare at the Open University. Two small but significant conferences were held, one on oral history, one on documentary history. The credit for organising these conferences, and for the production of this book, must go to Dorothy Atkinson and Jan Walmsley of the Open University and to Mark Jackson of the Wellcome Unit for the History of Medicine at the University of Manchester.

The conferences were something of a revelation. In an area of our recent past of which so little is known, every speaker's contribution was uniquely valuable. And yet it was the cumulative effects of these contributions which proved most fascinating. Dark corners were finally illuminated, only to reveal new, unsuspected, even darker crannies. New patterns began to take shape. What had been assumed to be uniform and monolithic was revealed as diverse and locally quirky. The majority of the contributions to these conferences, together with some others, are presented for the first time in this book, in the hope of enthusing others with the need to record, to conserve, to listen and, gradually, to understand.

Yet it is already almost too late. Before long the events of the twentieth century - extraordinary for the rise and eventual decline of institutions, responsible for swallowing and dominating the lives of so many and for fundamentally reshaping the experiences of families and communities - will no longer be able to be claimed by those most affected. Even historians will have little left to pick over, and the field will be left to any interested, and no doubt bemused, archaeologist of the future. And if this happens, we shall all be the losers. For this book is not just for professionals - the accounts presented here have touched the lives of us all. In every family photograph album there are faces which appear and then disappear, whose owners were briefly known and then forgotten, or not spoken of. So many stories worth the telling that it was, somehow, nobody's business to tell. And in the onrush of events, we seem still to turn away from our past, our present, our own futures, and to sever our connections to some of the most devastating events of this or any century.

Last week, for the first time, I visited the museum at the former concentration camp of Auschwitz, and nearby Birkenau, death camp for millions of Jews, Poles, Gypsies, and (as is often forgotten) sick and disabled people. Nothing in the United Kingdom can prepare you for this insight into the fate of disabled people under the Nazis. Yet many of the ideas, especially those concerned with creating genetic 'purity' and with the economics of supporting 'unproductive' people, were common to the rise of institutions whilst finding their final horrific expression in the death camps. After you pass under the notorious entrance arch ('Arbeit Macht Frei' - cynically 'Work will set you free'), the first building you enter displays a quotation from the Spanish-born American philosopher and poet George Santayana, which will serve as a suitable rationale for this book:

*'Those who cannot remember the past
are condemned to repeat it.'*

Paul Taylor
Associate Consultant
National Development Team, St. Peter's Court, Trumpet Street, Manchester

23 August 1996

Chapter 1

Introduction: Methods and Themes

Dorothy Atkinson, Mark Jackson and Jan Walmsley

This book aims to make a contribution to developing an interest in the history of learning disability[1] There is relatively little written in this area, much of it 'from above' in scholarly books and reports. As Joanna Ryan has pointed out, this has the effect of excluding people with learning disabilities from a history which is largely theirs: 'What history they do have is not so much theirs as the history of others acting either on their behalf, or against them.'[2]

The book aims to redress the balance between the two sides of history, tempering official and 'objective' accounts of the past with the memories and experiences of the people whose lives were shaped by past policies and practices. Their voices, hitherto often lost, are heard and acknowledged in this book. As personal histories are reclaimed, so the wider history of people with learning disabilities begins to be revealed. This is only a beginning but at least it *is* a beginning.

The book's distinctive contribution to the history of learning disability is twofold: firstly, it combines oral accounts with official documents and photographs; secondly, it concentrates primarily on encouraging the development of individual local, rather than national, histories of people with learning disabilities. More particularly, the book leads with the oral accounts of people with learning disabilities. Although later chapters also draw on oral history, they spread their net further to include the voices of staff and parents and a wide variety of documentary sources. We start with oral accounts of people with learning disabilities because we want to encourage readers to 'do' oral history - to recount the experiences of their own lives and to enable other people to recount theirs.

The growing interest in history

In recent years, there has been a tremendous expansion of interest in exploring the histories of people with what are now referred to as 'learning disabilities' or 'learning difficulties'. People with learning disabilities have themselves prepared extensive accounts of their lives, often with the assistance of friends and carers. Educational and co-ordinating organisations and support agencies have been striving to preserve a wealth of institutional and other records and to make them accessible to a wide variety of potential users. In addition, a number of professional historians and clinicians have started to research and write about various aspects of the history of learning disabilities.

This expanding interest in the history of learning disabilities can be traced to a number of factors. In the first instance, recent government policies have led to the closure of many long-stay institutions and to the removal of residents from those institutions 'into the community'. This shift from institutional care to community care has not been unproblematic. Debates about the relative merits of 'institutions' and 'communities' have persisted. Significantly, such debates have encouraged historians, practitioners, and policy-makers to reappraise the value of the institutional provisions that emerged in the late nineteenth and early twentieth centuries.

The recent demise of institutions (and the associated media coverage) has stimulated historical study in another way. As institutions have closed, vast quantities of institutional records have been uncovered. In some cases, these records have been destroyed. But increasingly, the managers of institutions, archivists and historians have collaborated in order to preserve those records (preferably in County Record Offices) and to make them accessible to as wide a range of readers as possible. As recent historical studies demonstrate (and as subsequent chapters in this book will make apparent), a rich array of previously untapped historical sources is now being exploited by historians.

A third factor that has contributed to the recent interest in the history of people with learning disabilities has been the emergence of advocacy (and more recently self-advocacy). This development has encouraged people with learning disabilities (and other marginalised groups) to recount their own experiences, to explore their own lives in and out of institutions and state care. Of course, this interest in advocacy (part of a much broader civil rights movement that emerged in the 1960s) is not new. Organisations such as Mencap, for example, have been advocating the needs of people with learning disabilities and their parents and carers for many years. (Incidentally, the fiftieth anniversary of 'Mencap' in 1996 was another stimulus to historical reflections.) However, in the late 1980s and early 1990s, particularly since the establishment of People First in 1984, advocates of the rights of people with learning disabilities have become more strident and more critical of the establishment. Interestingly, history has played a crucial role in these critiques by legitimating accounts of marginalisation and by challenging medical, social and political orthodoxies.

Recent interest in learning disabilities has also stemmed from changes within academic history and within the organisation and practice of medicine. Since the 1970s, and in particular since the work of E.P. Thompson, historians have been concerned not only with the lives of great men (or great wars) of the past but also with the lives of 'ordinary people'. Increasingly, historians have explored the lives and experiences of those men and women who were previously hidden from the historical picture. The growth of what has become known as 'history from below' has encouraged careful historical study of disadvantaged, marginalised and segregated sections of society, including people with learning disabilities. These developments have been further bolstered by increasing historical interest in using oral history as a means of exposing these otherwise forgotten lives.

Changes within the medical profession have also contributed to a growing interest in the history of learning disabilities. During the late nineteenth and early twentieth centuries, medical superintendents of institutions for 'mental defectives' (like asylum superintendents and other psychiatrists) remained distinct from mainstream medicine. Following the establishment of the National Health Service in 1948, psychiatrists and their institutions (most of which were renamed 'hospitals' at that time) became an integral part of an organised health service. This emergence of psychiatry as a legitimate speciality within medicine did much for the status of psychiatrists in general and for the status of psychiatrists specialising in the treatment and management of what was increasingly referred to as 'mental handicap'. Subsequently, the scientific study and treatment of learning disabilities has emerged as a distinct medical sub-speciality characterised by the establishment of academic units, by the founding of journals, and by the development of specific courses and career structures for medical and related practitioners. The emergence of a distinct speciality has also stimulated historical interest in this area.

Finally, historical interest in learning disabilities may have gained some impetus from the recent resurgence of biomedical, and particularly genetic, explanations of behaviour and disease. Evidence supposedly demonstrating the genetic basis for a variety of so-called deviant behaviours has accentuated tense debates about the relative influence of nature and nurture, and about the relative effects of heredity and the environment. More particularly, such discussions have raised the spectre of eugenics, an ideology closely associated with the origins of institutional care for 'mental defectives' at the end of the nineteenth century. Recent debates about the genetic basis of disease have therefore prompted a careful, and often critical, reappraisal of past theories and practices in this area.

Although there is clearly a blossoming interest in the history of what we now refer to as learning disabilities, and although historians, practitioners and archivists are more keenly aware of the potential value of historical records, there are as yet few historical studies focusing exclusively on learning disabilities. Until very recently, the history of learning disabilities has been covered in studies primarily concerned with quite different histories. The history of learning disabilities has thus been part of much broader studies of eugenics and genetics, of the development of education and special education, of psychology and psychiatry, and of developments in the organisation and policies of the mental health services in general.

These broad histories have contributed much to our general under-standing of the history of learning disabilities. However, they have often failed to explore the precise social, political and medical contexts in which certain forms of care and management have developed in particular places at particular times. In the last few years, however, this pattern has begun to change as increasing numbers of historians and practitioners have pursued the history of learning disabilities in particular locations and explored the myriad of social and political factors determining the evolution of services. As the bibliography in this volume suggests, historians on both sides of the Atlantic have recently started to explore in depth the rise and fall of different forms of institutional and community care, the changing patterns of legislation and state intervention, the emergence of special education, changing cultural constructions of disability and deviance, the involvement of psychologists, psychiatrists and other professional groups, as well as the broader social contexts in which policies and practices have evolved.

While these recent historical studies represent a welcome development, there are clearly a number of limitations to these current approaches and much further work is needed to build on these early studies. In the first instance, many historical studies of learning disabilities have been written primarily for academic historians. Consequently, they are not necessarily accessible to medical and related practitioners, to students, or to people with learning disabilities themselves. One of the central aims of this volume is to render both local and national historical records and historical methods available to a much wider audience. We hope that this encourages people to pursue their own historical interests.

Secondly, most historical studies have focused primarily on written sources. Although some historians have been keen to incorporate the results of interviews with the residents and staff of institutions, oral history remains to some extent subordinate to histories based on official written documents. As a result, there has been a tendency to produce supposedly objective histories that focus primarily on the accounts of events provided by contemporary politicians, doctors and administrators, rather than on the rich and challenging narratives offered by the subjects of medical and political policies.

A reliance on written records has produced another bias in many of these histories, that is an excessive focus on institutional histories, for which records are usually abundant, rather than on the experiences of individuals and families within the community, for which there are usually few records. A greater commitment to utilising the memories of people involved (as well as a wide range of other sources, such as photographs) would certainly help to eradicate this bias and to produce a more comprehensive picture of the histories of people with learning disabilities.

It is in this spirit that we have compiled the papers in this book. Written by a variety of people (including historians, practitioners and archivists) using a variety of historical sources, the chapters in this book necessarily tell a number of different stories about the how and the why of exploring the history of learning disabilities. Although these stories may differ in some ways, there are also many recurrent themes in the following chapters, such as the differential treatment of men and women, and the persistent marginalisation of people with learning disabilities. More particularly, however, a number of the chapters stress the importance of utilising as wide a range of historical sources as possible. Although we have privileged oral recollections from the residents and staff at institutions, we have done so for two specific reasons: first, in order to counteract a general tendency amongst historians to privilege documentary over oral sources; and, second, in order to emphasise that although all of these narratives need to be heard and understood, supposedly objective accounts based on official documents only come alive (or have meaning) in the context of the experiences of the people immediately involved.

Using oral sources

We include in the book two different sorts of oral accounts, autobiography and oral history. Chapter 2 comprises the autobiography of Mabel Cooper, whereas Chapter 3 by Rebecca Fido and Maggie Potts is an example of using oral history to tell the story of an institution through the eyes of the people who lived there. In this introductory chapter, we want to look, in particular, at Mabel Cooper's life story: at how and why it came to be written; and at what came out of it. However, we shall also draw on the work of Rebecca Fido and Maggie Potts (see Chapter 3), and others, to make some general points about involving people with learning disabilities in oral history.

Since we wrote her autobiography, Mabel and I (Dorothy Atkinson) have met to talk about it - what we did, and why, and what it means to her. We met to discuss these points so that Mabel's voice could be heard here too. She has 'written' her autobiography, which we include in full, but she has also reflected on the process of doing so, and her observations are included here. We are very grateful to Mabel for adding her voice to the voices of the editors.

Very few people write their stories unaided. Even the rich and famous often have a 'ghost writer' to work with them on their autobiography. If this applies to people who already have literacy skills then it obviously applies even more so to people with learning disabilities, for whom the written word is problematic. This means that life histories do literally need to be 'told', and told to someone else. That someone else - the ghost writer, or scribe, or interviewer - has two jobs to do: facilitate the telling of the story and to listen attentively to its telling (to be its 'audience'); and, later, to be its compiler and its writer (though not its owner).

But who decides, in the first place, that there is a story to tell? It could, of course, be the would-be biographer, researcher or historian who makes that link, and there are several examples in recent years of researchers involving people with learning disabilities in their life history research.[3] In the two examples we include in the book, however, the idea came from the people with learning disabilities themselves. Mabel had the idea many years ago that she wanted to tell her story - the only problem was in finding someone to work with her in doing it. She and I met by chance when, of all things, I was in search of people wanting to tell their stories, for possible inclusion in the Open University course I was then working on. The idea itself predated my arrival on the scene by around 20 years, although a start had been made in the interim with the making of a tape for someone else's college project.

Mabel explains where the idea came from and how it took root:

> Hazel had asked me to do it because she wanted to do it for a college, or something she was taking on, and I said, 'OK, but will you put it on a tape recorder for me, and I will try and make a little book out of it, because there's a lot more than that on it.' And because I'd already done that tape with Hazel I thought, well, if I find somebody else, I'll ask somebody to help me a bit more.

> I think it's good really, to think about what happened to you when you were a child. I think it's great. It's something. I know Joey Deacon[4] did that. I was in Whyteleafe House[5] by then but I knew about it. It was an idea, but it's only an idea unless you get somebody to help you. It was just luck that I met you.

In the oral history project described by Fido and Potts in Chapter 3, the idea for sharing memories of the past came from the residents themselves. They were, in their later years, involved in a self-advocacy group, and the idea had emerged through their group discussions. Fido and Potts became their interviewers and their scribes.

The recounting of life stories, individual or shared, autobiographical or biographical, is a social process. It occurs within a relationship between the teller and the listener. Stories may be told on a one-to-one basis, as with Mabel and me, and Fido and Potts in their interviews with seventeen hospital residents. But they may also be told in group settings, where shared memories as well as individual accounts can be told and recorded.[6] It is important that a relationship of trust exists between the people involved, and that the person who listens does so attentively, sensitively and with respect. There is another important consideration for the novice oral historian and that is being well informed and well prepared. There are a number of useful publications and guidelines available now which are best consulted *before* the first interview.[7]

There also needs to be an understanding and agreement about confidentiality and ownership. In many instances, people who choose to tell their stories also choose to reveal who they are - indeed, this is a source of pride. Not everyone feels this way, however, and the people in Fido and Potts' oral history project preferred to remain anonymous. Even the name of their institution remains disguised and is referred to simply as 'The Park'. The important thing is not to assume what people want, but to find out from them what degree of confidentiality and anonymity is thought necessary.

Who owns a life story - the person who tells it (and whose life it is) or the person who records and writes it? This is an important point. Often people who contribute to research projects, through talking about themselves and their lives in interviews, are not the ultimate owners of their stories - the ownership somehow passes to the researcher who tape records their stories, and later transcribes and analyses them, and compiles them into research themes or linked accounts in a published article or book. People with learning difficulties may be particularly vulnerable to such loss of ownership, so this is an issue to be addressed in any auto/biographical work or oral history research.[8] People do have ownership rights in relation to their own stories.

What about the 'rights', if any, of the scribe who works with someone to write their story? Mabel had thought about the question of ownership in relation to her life story, and this became a theme which she pursued in our reflective discussion about her book:

M: I would like you to put your name in it, in a part of it. I think it should be there; after all, you've helped me to do the work.

D: But it's your story.

M: Yes, it doesn't matter, but I would like your name in it, wherever, you just say, and put your name into it and the college.

D: That's very generous.

M: Well, I think if it wasn't for you, and the college, I wouldn't have had it done. It would have been something I wouldn't have been able to do on my own, so I would like you to put your name into it.

What motivated Mabel and the oral historians from 'The Park' to explore their own histories? In many ways, their personal motivation would probably match that of any other autobiographer; to reflect on, and make sense of, their lives and put past events into perspective. This is autobiography as life review. But Mabel and the others were also motivated by their wish to tell other people what it was like for them. This suggests a sense of history - an awareness that they were key witnesses of an historical era which was now passing.

Mabel expressed this historical awareness in this way:

It's an achievement with me being in St Lawrence's[9] for so many years, and not knowing anything else but St Lawrence's. I thought it would be nice to let people know what it was like, and to let people know how difficult it was for someone with a learning disability, and who was stuck away because of that. I thought that people outside should know these things because they're not aware of it at the moment and I think it would be nice.

Similarly, Potts and Fido have described elsewhere how the participants in their oral history project developed a sense of history:

As people have talked they have learned to value their own history and become increasingly confident and determined that the public should know what life has been like for them. [10]

There is more to telling, and writing, a story than the interview itself, however central that is in the process. This applies especially if a tape recorder is used, because much of the work continues after and between interviews. The more informal and conversational the approach taken in the interview - and this is important in helping the person relax and feel comfortable - the more complicated the task becomes afterwards. The main aim of the interviews is to cover the various milestones, events and turning points in someone's life, but not necessarily in the 'right' order from childhood and schooldays to adult life. Memories are not always organised in this way, and people may approach some events - particularly ones with painful associations - in a more circumspect way than through a straight chronological account.

The interviewer's task after each interview is to transcribe the words from the tape into written words on paper. Somehow that untidy and unorganised 'raw' account then needs to be tidied up and put into some sort of coherent narrative. That process needs to be a shared one. The sharing can be at the transcription stage, where the full account is read back and the story-teller has a full say in the editing and re-organising process.[11] More usually, the researcher or historian does some preliminary work on the raw material first, organising it into a chronological sequence and/or into themes, removing repetitions and doing some minor editing. This revised version is then read back for additions and alterations. This is how I worked with Mabel on her autobiography. Similarly, in their chapter, Fido and Potts describe how they held 'readings' so that people could listen to how their accounts of their lives sounded when put together.

There are a number of critical advantages to exploring people's lives and experiences in these ways. One of the most important things for Mabel is that her story is written down. Although she cannot read it for herself, it is important that other people can do so. It represents a sense of achievement. It is undoubtedly a source of pride. But above all she has, as she explains below, 'something to show' for the life she has lived. The institution itself has subsequently been demolished but Mabel's life story remains. She says she will keep it as long as she lives. In its published form in this book, it will live on beyond Mabel's life-time as a testimony to the era in which she lived and the system in which she was caught for much of her life.

This is what Mabel's book means to her:

> I think it was nice for me to be able to do something, so that I could
> say 'I've done it'. It made me feel that it was something I had done.
> You've got something so that you can say, 'This is what happened to
> me'. Some of it hurts, some of it's sad, some of it I'd like to
> remember. My story means a lot to me because I can say, 'This is
> what happened to me', if anyone asks. So it's great, and I will
> keep it for the rest of my life. I will keep the book.

A life story operates at more than one level. Mabel is aware of this. She
is reflective in the story itself, standing back from what happened to
her personally to think about the wider implications of past policies
and practices. When we met again to discuss her account of her life in
the context of this book, Mabel talked more about the wider social and
historical context in which her experiences find their place. She pursued
three themes: institutions existed because of people's fear of difference;
she was sent to one because of the policies operating in this country at
a particular point in time; and once inside an institution she, and
others, were in an enclosed and separate world.

These points are covered below in Mabel's own words. We hope the work
she has done will inspire others to follow in her footsteps.

Fear of difference

> For people like me, and a lot more, you know, people were
> frightened of us. So in them days they said OK, there's nowhere for
> you, you get shut away in the big institutions. If people are
> different then other people get frightened. I still see it. People are
> frightened of people like me, and a lot more, because we're
> different.

> I go into the schools now, and talk to the children, and I've been
> invited back to the schools, so for the next three weeks I'm off
> into the schools. But, you know, they were frightened, they even
> told me, the children. They're frightened of people what are
> different.

An accident of birth

> I got into the system very early. It was only because I had the
> learning disability, they've found that out now. I was born at the
> wrong time. Because I always say to the children, if I was young
> again I would have liked to have gone to the school, and learnt all

the things I don't know now. The only thing is, when you start
going in places like that, they label you and that's it.

An enclosed world

St Lawrence's was all I knew for years, it was all I knew until 15 or
16 years ago. When you're in there you don't know anything else.
There was nice people like Eva, she was nice, I got on with her. You
had your doubts about some of them but in the end you knew
they had to do the work, so you can't, it's not their fault, it's just
they were there...

The uses of history

Finally, it is reasonable to ask 'Why history?' Does the study of history
have any use, or is it merely an idle pastime? Mabel Cooper's answer to
that question is that it definitely does have a use, because it enables her
to say of her book 'I've done it', and that she has 'something to show' for
her life. Both Mabel and the contributors to the oral history of 'The
Park' express the belief that people should know what life has been like
for them.

In addition, the study of history can contribute to a sense of identity. A
sense of our own history as individuals is important for a sense of
personal identity; a sense of the history of a group to which we belong,
whether we like it or not, by virtue of our label, may be equally important
for a sense of group identity. Other groups of people whose lives have
been left out of the mainstream historical narrative have recognised the
importance of discovering that they too have a history. Jewish women
in London, introducing a collection of biographies, insisted that one of
their aims was to 'challenge the stereotyped assumptions about who
Jewish women were and what their lives were like'.[12] Other people have
used the study of the past as a means of giving a sense of direction:

We need the past in order to be able to understand
ourselves. We need it in order to believe in our future. If we
have come from nowhere, where are we going to?[13]

Stories like Mabel Cooper's are a first step in challenging stereotypes
and creating a sense of history of people with learning disabilities as a
group with a set of distinctive experiences.

But can any lessons be learned from history? As editors, we would
cautiously suggest that they can, if we are prepared to heed them. At the

extreme, it is important to recognise that people with learning difficulties were subjected to extermination policies in Nazi Germany.[14] An awareness of this should encourage us to empathise with the 'People First' message which is the watchword of self-advocacy organisations in this country and elsewhere. Mabel speaks of fear as a motive for shutting people away in institutions. We hope that information will serve as an important antidote to fear.

What of institutions? Can history teach lessons about them? Institutions have too often been polarised as either 'good' or 'bad'. The advocates of institutions portray them as safe havens where people with severe disabilities can live away from the dangers of the outside world. Those who are opposed to institutions regard them as inevitably oppressive places, routinised, depersonalising and often abusive. As Andy Stevens argues in his chapter, however, it is high time that the origins and role of institutions in the history of learning disability are examined as an historical phenomenon, rather than being used as a weapon in contemporary political battles.

As editors, we hope that this collection will motivate readers to find out more about the 'forgotten lives' of people with learning disabilities and their families and to draw their own lessons from history. What does the history look like? The chart which follows this introductory chapter sets out the main events in the last 100 years, tracing the events in Mabel Cooper's own life against trends and developments in the second half of the century.

Notes

1. We use the terms 'people with learning disabilities' and 'people with learning difficulties' interchangeably throughout the book. Individual authors also use historical terms specific to the period in question, such as 'mental deficiency', 'mental handicap', without any insult intended.

2. J. Ryan, *The Politics of Mental Handicap*, (Harmondsworth, Penguin,1980), p.85.

3. See, for example; J.Walmsley, 'Life History Interviews with People with Learning Disabilities', Oral History, 23, 1, (1995), 71-77; T.Booth, & W.Booth, *Parenting under Pressure: Mothers and fathers with learning difficulties,* (Buckingham, Open University Press, 1994).

4. J. Deacon, *Tongue Tied*, (London, NSMHC, 1977).

5. Whyteleafe House was the name of the half-way house which Mabel Cooper lived in as part of her return to the community.

6. See, for example, D.Atkinson, "I got put away". Group-based reminiscence with people with learning difficulties', in J.Bornat (ed.), *Reminiscence Reviewed: Perspectives, evaluations, achievements*, (Buckingham, Open University Press, 1994).

7. Useful publications and guidelines include: Paul Thompson, *The Voice of the Past: Oral History* (2nd edition, Oxford University Press, 1988); Paul Thompson and Rob Perks, *An Introduction to the Use of Oral History in the History of Medicine*, (London, National Sound Archive, 1993); Paul Thompson 'Oral History and the History of Medicine: a Review', *Social History of Medicine*, 4, 2, (1991), 371-83; Steve Humphries and Pamela Gordon, *Back To Your Roots: Recording Your Family History*, (BBC Publications,1993); Steve Humphries and Pamela Gordon, *Out of Sight: Recording the Life Stories of Disabled People*, (Channel 4 Television, 1992).

8. See, for example, the discussion by Joanna Bornat and Jan Walmsley, 'Oral history with vulnerable groups', (unpublished paper, delivered at International Oral History Society Conference, New York, 1994).

9. This is a reference to St Lawrence's Hospital, Caterham, Surrey.

10. Maggie Potts and Rebecca Fido, '*A Fit Person To Be Removed*': *Personal Accounts of Life in a Mental Deficiency Institution*, (Northcote House, 1991), p.12.

11. This process is described in the introduction to *Positive Tales* (LivingArchive Press, Milton Keynes, 1996), a collection of auto-biographical accounts by people with learning disabilities.

12. Jewish Women in London Group, *Generations of Memories: Voices of Jewish Women*, (London, Women's Press, 1989).

13. Hall Carpenter Archives, *Inventing Ourselves: Lesbian Life Stories* (London, Routledge, 1989), p.1.

14. Michael Burleigh, *Death and Deliverance: 'Euthanasia' in Germany c.1900-1945* (Cambridge University Press, 1994).

Learning Disability in Britain in the Twentieth Century: Chart of major developments

	Legislation and National Events	Major Policy Developments	Publications	Professional Parent and User Groups	Changing Labels	Mabel Cooper's Life
1900	1908 Report of Royal Commission on Care and Control of the Feeble-Minded	1902 Sandlebridge Colony opened. 1907 formation of Eugenics Education Society	1908 Tredgold 1st edition (see bibliography)		Use of terms 'idiot', 'imbecile', 'feeble-minded' and 'moral imbecile' in Mental Deficiency Act 1913	
1910	1913 Mental Deficiency Act 1914 Elementary Education Act					
1920	1924 Wood Committee appointed 1927 Mental Deficiency (Amendment) Act	1920s-1940s major local authority colony (hospital) building	1929 Wood Report published	Central Association or Mental Welfare, major voluntary organisation active in field of 'mental deficiency'	'Mental defective' and 'mental deficiency' most common general terms 1900-c. 1950; 'moral defective' replaced 'moral imbecile' in 1927 Mental Deficiency Act	

	Legislation and National Events	Major Policy Developments	Publications	Professional Parent and User Groups	Changing Labels	Mabel Cooper's Life
1930	1930s Campaign for Voluntary Sterilisation	1931 Bromham Colony opened 1931 South Ockendon colony admitted its 'first mental defectives'	1934 Brock Report recommends sterilisation 1937 Cyril Burt's 'The Backward Child' published 1938 Lionel Penrose 'Colchester Report' (a Clinical and Genetic Study of 1280 cases of Mental Defect)			
1940	1944 Education Act 1948 NHS took over hospital services.	1948 Mental Welfare Officers appointed to work outside hospitals		1946 Association of Parents of Backward Children founded (later Mencap)		1945 Mabel Cooper born
1950	Late 1940s-1950s major Occupation (Day) Centre expansion		1951 NCCL's '50,000 Outside The Law' highlighted affront to civil liberties represented by detention of 'mental defectives'		Use of term 'sub-normal' started in USA	1952 Mabel sent to St Lawrence's Hospital, Caterham

Legislation and National Events	Major Policy Developments	Publications	Professional Parent and User Groups	Changing Labels	Mabel Cooper's Life
1953-9 Royal Commission on Mental Health	1955 Botton village founded - first Camphill Community		1954 Assn. of Parents of Backward Children invited to give evidence to Royal Commission		
			1955 Guild of Teachers of Backward Children founded	'Backward' came into vogue as a descriptive term	
1959 Mental Health Act		1961 Erving Goffman's 'Asylums' critique of institutions		1959 Mental Health Act used terms 'subnormal' and 'severely subnormal'	1960 Moved to adult ward (age 15)
1960	1961 Enoch Powell, Min. of Health, says mental hospitals will close in 15 years				
	1960s Hospital scandals - Ely, Farleigh, South Ockendon, Normansfield	1967 Stanley Segal's 'No child is ineducable' paved the way for education for all			
		1969 earliest publications on normalisation by Bank-Mikkelson & Bengt Nirje (Sweden)			

1970	Legislation and National Events	Major Policy Developments	Publications	Professional Parent and User Groups	Changing Labels	Mabel Cooper's Life
			1969 Morris's 'Put Away' put case against hospitals			
	1970 Education Act made education universal		1972 Wolf Wolfensberger's 'The Principal of Normalisation in Human Services' published in Toronto		The Mentally Handicapped' came into use	Mabel continued to live in St Lawrence'sHospital
	Late 1960s to early 1980s major hostel building era	1971 Better Services for the Mentally Handicapped advocated care in the community		1972 'Our Life' first national conference of people with learning difficulties	1972 BILD formed as Institute of Mental Subnormality	
	1970 Chronically Sick and Disabled Persons Act	1975 National Development Group founded to advise on policy and practice		1974 Disability Alliance founded		

	Legislation and National Events	Major Policy Developments	Publications	Professional Parent and User Groups	Changing Labels	Mabel Cooper's Life
						1976 Mabel left St Lawrence's Hospital and moved to Whyteleafe House, a hostel
			1978 Publication of Warnock Report which came out in favour of integration of some children with special needs in mainstream schools			
			1979 Jay Report emphasised principles of community based care			
1980	1981 Education Act laid down that children should be educated in mainstream schools or classes wherever possible	1980s–1990s Group home era	1980 'An Ordinary Life' Kings Fund publication advocated 'an ordinary life', normalisation		'People with Mental Handicap' became the preferred term c. 1980	
		1983 All Wales Strategy for development of services to mentally handicapped people		1984 first People First group in England	1985 'People with learning difficulties' adopted by self advocacy group and sympathisers	1984 Mabel moved in with a family in Croydon. 1985 moved to live with a second family. 1986 moved to live with a carer (and had her own room).
	1988 Disabled Persons (Services Consultations and Representation) Act		1986 Open University's 'Mental Handicap: Patterns for Living' course published			

Legislation and National Events	Major Policy Developments	Publications	Professional Parent and User Groups	Changing Labels	Mabel Cooper's Life
1990					
1990 National Health Service and Community Care Act	1989 Sandlebridge Colony closed	1989 'Caring for People' White Paper set out principles for shift to community care in NHS and Community Care Act			1990 Mabel joined People First, London
1995 Disability Discrimination Act	1994 South Ockendon St Lawrence's Hospitals closed		1994 first 'England People First' Conference	c1990 Department of Health officially adopted term 'people with learning disabilities'	1992 Mabel moved to live with present carer
	Mixed economy of care - state, vol. orgs., private sector, family - became ideal	1996 OU's 'Equal People' published		Mencap's 50th anniversary	1993 Mabel attended People First Conference, Canada
					1994 Mabel elected as chair of People First
					1996 Mabel attended national launch of 'Equal People'

Chapter 2

Mabel Cooper's Life Story

Summary

This is Mabel Cooper's autobiography, constructed from tape recorded interviews. Her life reflects the changing policies and practices of the last 50 years. As a child she lived first in a children's home and later in a long-stay hospital. Many years later she left hospital for a life in the community, where she became involved in self-advocacy. The telling of her story is a major landmark in Mabel's life. She hopes that its appearance in this book will inspire other people with learning difficulties to find ways of telling their own life stories.

Family

I didn't know at that time that I had anybody. A lady called Mary Mason, she was a nurse in St Lawrence's hospital, she helped me find my auntie. Auntie Edith. Then I went visiting her. She's still alive and I still go and see her sometimes.

I've got five cousins as well which I searched for when my auntie was taken ill. Auntie Edith gave me the numbers for them. One lives in Zimbabwe, in South Africa, one lives in Croydon and the others all live in Bedford. I go and visit them from time to time.

It was a long time ago when I found my auntie. I was in the hospital then. She told me my mother had died. She was my auntie's sister. I don't know my father. My auntie doesn't know him. She said they were married.

My Gran lived in Croydon. My auntie moved and went to Bedford. My mother lived outside Bedford.

Childhood

When I was little I lived in another place like St Lawrence's, but it was just for children. This was in Bedford. It used to be run by nuns. And that had bars up at the windows as well, because they used to call them places madhouses. It was in Bedford. They haven't got it any more, they've vanished it.

I moved to St Lawrence's when I was seven, because they only took children what went to school in this home. And I never went to school, so I had to move. In them days they give you a test. You went to London or somewhere because they'd give you a test before they make you go anywhere. It used to be a big place, all full of offices and what-have-you. Because they said you should be able to read when you're seven or eight. I couldn't read, I hadn't been to school. That was 1952, I was seven years old.

The Hospital
First impressions
When I first went in there, even just getting out of the car you could hear the racket. You think you're going to a madhouse. When you first went there you could hear people screaming and shouting outside. It was very noisy but I think you do get used to them after a little while because it's like everywhere that's big. If there's a lot of people you get a lot of noise, and they had like big dormitories, didn't they? And the children were just as noisy, in the children's home, and they were all the same sort of people.

St Lawrence's Hospital

I went to St Lawrence's in 1952. I went to A2, that was the admissions ward. They didn't used to have many in there, they used to just take the new ones what came in. You were only there for about a week or two weeks. And they moved you on to another ward where there was all children. I stayed there till I was 15 and then I went to another ward where I was with adults.

There was bars on the windows when I first went to St Lawrence's, it was just like a prison. Of course it was called a nuthouse in them days, so it used to have bars on it. You couldn't open the windows. Well, you could, but not far enough to get out of them. You didn't have toys, no toys whatsoever. You couldn't have toys because they would just get broken and thrown through the bars in the window, and get caught in them.

It was big. There were lots and lots of wards. On the female side it was A to H. On the male side it was A to D. They all had about 75 people in. And then there was little houses on the grounds and they had about 50 people in.

School/work
There used to be children, there used to be two wards of children. One for little boys and one for girls. There was no school there, they only let you use your hands by making baskets and doing all that sort of thing. That's all you did. In them days they said you wasn't able enough to learn so you didn't go to school you went to like a big ward and they had

tables. You just went there and made the baskets or what-have-you. Because in them days they said you wasn't capable enough to learn to do anything else, so that's what you did.

So in St Lawrence's they never went to school. They went and made baskets. If you didn't do that you went to one of the work places or in the laundry, or stayed in the ward and did nothing. As you got older you could stay doing baskets or you could go down the laundry or the work-shops in the grounds. I made a friend of Eva and she did one of the workshops where I worked. I worked on the baskets. A lot of them used to stay on the ward, or go round and sit round on the field and didn't do anything. Because really, who wants to work in an old laundry? Not many people did that.

Some of them went out to work, where you'd go and try somewhere. Some of the people I used to be friends with did that. Gloria done it, my friend Gloria, because she was in hospital. She went to Purley Hospital and worked. She went out before me, she went out a long time before me. She stayed out, she never came back. If anything went wrong when they were out they used to go and pick them up, and bring them back.

Clothes
The worst thing was, I couldn't wear my own clothes, you had to wear other people's. Because you never, you never got your own because the beds were too close together, so you didn't have a locker or anything, you just went to this big cupboard and helped yourself. There might be six piles of dresses in this big cupboard. They had all the clothes in and you'd just go and help yourself to the clothes you want. I didn't like it, that you wasn't even allowed to wear your own clothes in them days.

Of course they had their own shoes, you couldn't wear your own shoes in them days, you had to wear their shoes and they were horrible. They made them there, in the hospital. You never went out for anything because they did everything in the hospital. The clothes were made in the hospital, in the sewing rooms.

They did everything there, they made their own bread and everything; they had a bakery. They had a farm. They used to have cows and sheep there.

Aerial view of St. Lawrence's Hospital

Separation of men and women

On the male side you see they're different. The male side was different to the female side, there was more on the female side than there was on the male. There was a lot more on the female side. You couldn't mix with the men. You could go to a dance but you'd have men one side, women the other. You could dance with them, but they had to go back men one side, women the other side. Even in the dance hall there was two loads of staff in the middle, one full of women and one full of men, and you just danced around the staff in the middle.

The female staff were on one side, on one row and male on the other, and you just danced around them. You could go over and dance, and they had to go back to one side and I went back on the other.

Money

In them days you didn't have proper money. If they give you any money it's green, it's like little green coins. You can't use it outside, you can't buy anything outside, you could only use it in their canteen. You could just go down and spend it in the canteen. It was only for sweets.

Running away/hiding
If I got upset I'd just run away, for a couple of hours. You couldn't go out, so if I got upset I would just go off, and I would come back when I was ready. I wouldn't stay out the night or anything like that but I would come back when I was ready, and then I'd be all right. I would go round the field because their field is quite big at the back. And you could just sit there, there were seats and you could just sit and be on your own. And I'd come back when I was ready.

Life on the ward
Loads of people used to live in St Lawrence's. There were loads of them there. In a ward there was about 75, men or women - you couldn't get men with women. I was in a ward with 75 other women, and the beds were that small, they were that close to one another. Of course they had some in the grounds as well, and they had fifty in those places.

Because there was too many in the hospital they did no cooking in the ward kitchen. If you think, 75 in one ward, they couldn't do cooking in the wards. They had a kitchen there but they did no cooking. They couldn't teach you to do anything because there wasn't enough time for the nurses. They used to go off at half one and another lot used to come on and used to stay till nine, and then they would go off and a night nurse would come on. During the day there would be three different lots of staff.

The ward was blocked off, there was doors. You weren't allowed to sit on your beds. The beds were that close to one another, so you couldn't have anything private. I didn't have anything of my own, because they would get pinched, the other patients would pinch them.

Of course you wasn't allowed to stand on the corridors or do anything like that. If you didn't go into one of the workshops, or the laundry, or the basket making, or digging up gardens then you sat on the ward. Sometimes I did that, because it's all I knew. If that's all you know it's very difficult not to do anything else.

In the hospital you used to have to be in by eight, because of the night nurses at 9 o'clock. You had to be in bed by nine. If you wasn't in at 8 o'clock you'd have to go in one of the other wards and ask them to come and open the doors, especially if they haven't got a night nurse in one of the wards. In two of the wards they didn't have night nurses so if you wasn't in at 8 o'clock then you'd have to go and ask one of the other wards to open the door and let you in. You soon got told off in the morning if you did that. I never done that but it did use to happen. I stayed out of a lot of trouble, but some of the others did things what they shouldn't be doing, like staying out late. I don't think it's worth getting into trouble, you might just as well do what they want. And the day will come when you can go out and get about on your own.

You had to get up at half six, seven o'clock. In my time you didn't have choices. You just did as they said.

Meals

We all ate on the ward together, but not with the staff. The food was vile, I didn't like it. They used to bring the dinners up at 11 o'clock and they used to sit and talk till 12 or half past. The dinners were horrible. There was no choices. My friend Eva, she used to be one of the nurses, she used to heat it up for us.

Relationships

I made a friend and she used to work in one of the workshops in the hospital, and I used to go there. This was Eva. She was the staff, she was one of the nurses. Eva used to sit and talk to me sometimes but otherwise you don't get anybody because they'd say they hadn't got the time.

I made a few friends with some of the patients. There was Gloria, Gloria Ferris, I made friends with her. I still see her. I go out every Saturday with her.

A lot of them got married. I didn't have many men friends.
I never had any visitors in the hospital, nobody at all, never.

I found my auntie because she wrote to me once or twice in the hospital. And I said I would like to visit this aunt and one of the nurses, Mary Mason, she said, "Oh, I'll find out about it. I'll get a pass and I'll take you." So she did. We phoned up, she phoned up auntie and I went to see her, and now I do go and see her regularly. She was living in Bedford then. She lived in London for a little while, and then she moved out of London and went to Bedford.

Trips out

You weren't allowed out of the hospital. You had to write up and ask could you leave the grounds. You had to ask the medical or write to the doctor and ask them. You couldn't just go across the road and look at the shops, it wasn't allowed not unless you wrote up and asked. I didn't go out because I got so used to not going out. You'd get lost if you're not used to it.

If you wanted to go out they would give you a card. And every time you went out, you could only go out from 2 o'clock till four. If you wasn't back by four then you would be in trouble. You could never go out on your own, you always had to go with somebody, like one of the staff. You could write up and get a pass for a Saturday afternoon, but you had to get permission every time. They would watch to see if you come in after four. If you didn't get back, they'd give you till six and if you weren't back then they would ring the police.

In the old days, you had to be very crafty, you had to be one ahead of them. You could get down the pipe. The pipes used to be very big and if you was on the third floor upstairs, and you went down on to the fire escape, there used to be a big pipe. You used to get down in that because it was wide, it was wide enough for you to fit. So they could get out of the bottom because the hole at the bottom was big enough for them to get out of. And it led you outside the gate which you couldn't get out of otherwise, because that was always locked.

You could go round the boundary. There used to be a big old church, it's not there any more they've built a school on there. You could go round the back of the church and by the fence there used to be an opening. We used to go out through that way and then get back in through that way. You could only get as far as the shop down the road, that was all. You could just go round and look, and come back again. At least it was something that you could do, till you got caught. I didn't do it much, I did it once or twice. Nobody else knew it was there.

In the hospital they used to have a church so you never went out of the hospital to go to church because they had one in there, on the corridor. I never went to church. I don't go now only because I can't read. And for me, it's ridiculous so I just don't go. In the hospital church the men sat on one side and the women sat on the other. They used to pass letters in through the church, underneath the seat the letters used to go. The women used to pass letters across. I never went to church so I never did that. You could go round the fields and, if there was no staff about, then you could do it that way but otherwise you couldn't.

If you went on holiday with the hospital you sat on the grass and didn't do anything. They just used to sit on the grass if it was a nice day. You didn't go on the beach or anything. We went to like a holiday thing and they had green huts and they used to go to them. They didn't used to take anybody else. They just used to take people from hospitals. We never saw anybody else because they didn't encourage it.

Punishment

They had a ward up in the hospital G3 and they used to put people in there. They used to get locked up. I never was in G3 because I never run away or anything like that. They used to make you wear your bed slippers and then you couldn't run away. The door was locked, but you could get out. If you got out though you couldn't get back in so you had to ring the bell. G3 was for women, D3 was for men.

Reflections

In them days if you had learning difficulties or anything that's where they used to put you. They didn't say, "Oh, you could go into a house and somebody would look after you." They would just say, "You, you've gotta go into a big hospital" and that's it. Years ago, if you wasn't married and you had a baby that was a disgrace and they would say, "Oh the mother goes to a workhouse or a loony bin" as they had in them days, or the mother went into a workhouse or a loony bin and the child was put in care. I think that's why there was more women.

In the hospital if you wanted to do anything or to go anywhere it was so much of a bind because you had to keep asking someone to write for you, so a lot of the time I never did. I got used to the hospital. Not really because I wanted to be there, it was because that's what I knew. That's all you knew, you didn't know anything else not like I do now.

A lot of people, especially people like me, we always think if they didn't have enough money to keep us outside they would say, "Right, you all have to go back in the hospital" and open them again. It's important they knock them down and then people like me and a lot more will know that won't happen. I think it worries a lot of people like me because they are still standing there because they could say "OK, we're going to open all that again and all the people what were there go back up there". Of course it saves them a lot of money. I know they have turned a lot of St Lawrence's off, they've built houses on there. Some of it's gone, but there's still a lot there[1].

Leaving Hospital

Whyteleafe House

Whyteleafe House was the same as St Lawrence's, the only difference is that it was a house. It was still a big place. It was no different because they still had nurses and what-have-you. You still had 50 people. It was all women. I shared a room with six others.

Whyteleafe House used to be for people what used to go out to work, they didn't take anybody else. And then they said, "Oh well, we haven't got enough people now what go out to work, we'll have to change it and put other people there". That's how I got to go to Whyteleafe House.

The hospital used to bring me in the car and they used to take me back to Whyteleafe in the car. I lived at Whyteleafe House, they used to pick me up at the house and take me to the hospital for the day. At night time they used to take me back. I never went on the bus that we go on now. If you didn't go out, like me and a few of them, you still had to wait for someone to go with you. Eventually I just said could I go and try myself and they said I could. I went by myself but they don't like it.

I was about 31 when I went to Whyteleafe House. I've been out of St Lawrence's 16 years now. I asked to leave. My friend, Eva, she wrote and asked. She said I might be able to cope a bit. She got in touch with the social worker what used to be in the hospital. If you wanted to go to work or anything then they would just get in contact with one of the social workers.

First impressions of the outside world
When I first came out of there I thought the children were midgets. People have laughed because they said to me, "Was that the difficultist part of coming out of there and finding children are midgets?" I never saw children, only children in wheelchairs and what-have-you, not children running about and doing all the things they're doing. So really the children fascinated me, seeing them it really did fascinate me.

I'd never been on a bus or on a train. Because you never went. These are all the things you didn't do. It's not like ordinary people going out and doing what they want to do. In them places, you didn't. So going on a train or going on the underground all them are new to me. In fact going on the underground and on the moving stairs and all that is quite new to me. I'm used to the bus now because I go so much. I don't have to buy a ticket, I've got a pass.

Early days in the community
I lived with a family in Caterham Valley but she used to keep having nervous breakdowns. She used to be ever so funny. And then, because there was nobody in the house when I went home one day, I got frightened and ran off. I went to Eva's house but I couldn't stay there so Eva phoned up and I went in where I worked, at the old people's home. I lived there, stayed there. I used to help look after the old people in Caterham. I used to help them do the cleaning. I lived there for a little while, and then they said, "Oh, you can't live here any more". They said, "You know, it's not really for you".

So I went to live with another lady, she had a Down's syndrome boy. A social worker, a man, decided this, but that was only supposed to have been for a short time. It was at Old Lodge Lane. I was there for a year and a half, then I went to Isabel's. I went because the other lady only wanted someone to play with her little boy and I didn't want to do that, not really. I don't want to keep somebody company.

When I first went to Isabel's she found me a morning job but they were again being a bit difficult because Isabel had to keep coming up and getting social workers to come and talk to them. I just gave it up. There was only me and Anne in the beginning at Isabel's. And then she said she was gonna have another one, and she had Gloria. Then they started to get more and more and more, till there was 13 living there.

I had my own front door key at Isabel's and she made sure always that you had money in your pocket. I had my own room and since I'd been at Isabel's I'd got my own telly and my own tape recorder. I stayed at Isabel's six years and a half and I thought, well, now it's time for me to adventure a bit more. Gloria got like me, she asked to move out of Isabel's because there was too many, like I did, and she went to live with two sisters.

I thought it was time I adventured. I got friendly with a lady called Anne Evans, one of the boarding-out ladies and a friend of Gloria's. I went to dinner one day with Gloria and Anne and I said to Anne "Do you know I'm thinking of asking to move out of Isabel's? It's just too noisy". There were 13 people then. I stayed as long as I thought I could stand it. And I said, right, this is enough, and I asked. I said to Anne, "I am thinking of moving, definitely" and she said, "Oh, leave it with me and I'll sort it out for you". I went to a few places and I said no, and then I went to Mary's.

I've been at Mary's a year, gone a year now. I moved there in May 1992.

Life Now

Mary is my carer now. She buys the clothes for me because I find that's difficult. Mary does it for me because my eyesight's not that brilliant and the writing's so small. I can't read the labels so Mary does it. Jean lives at Mary's, she's all right, she helped me write a letter last night. She can't walk very much but otherwise she's OK. So I've got Jean and I've got Mary, so there is people there.

Gloria lives in South Croydon with Nora. Nora is like Mary, a carer. So Gloria lives there and on Saturdays I go there to see her. We're good friends but I don't think I could live with Gloria. And I've got Flo, I've got quite a few friends what don't live, what hasn't been in hospital - but I've got some what have.

I go down the seaside, I go places. I just tell Mary I'm off and I go. Because when I first came out I had to learn to get on the bus and go to the places I want to do. I taught myself to go to Brighton. I had to. They showed me what train to get on. And then I didn't sit on the grass, I went to the fair because I like the fair. That was new to me as well. I even go to Margate. You have to go to Victoria and get a train from Victoria.

I joined People First two or three years ago, when Isabel asked me would I like to join. There were about ten people when it first started in Croydon, now there's loads. I didn't join in very much at the first time or for a couple of weeks, something like that. Then one of the men what was chairperson, he didn't turn up so they asked me would I take it on. So I said, "Oh, all right, I'll take it on for one week". And one week got more weeks than ever. This was last year sometime.

Because of being in the People First Group I went to Canada. That was the biggest conference yet, that was bigger than Mencap put together. That was good, Canada is one of the good ones. But I think I would have liked somebody else to come because it would have been more exciting with somebody else. Declan said it would have been nice for somebody else from Croydon to come as well. I do a few jobs for Declan, like going out talking to people, and help tidying their office, and doing all the little jobs they need to do on a Monday. Declan pays and keeps the money for me, so it pays for my trips and what-have-you.

The group I'm doing now is coming out in the community. Me and another fellow is going to do that, two days a week for three months. Two days every week, for three months. We've also been into one of the day centres in London but a lot of people, they don't understand. One of them we had to ask could they go out because she was making so much noise. But I said to them, "You know, she must be allowed to come back again", I said, "because she's out this time she mustn't stay out, she must come back and join in". They said, "Could the carers come in?" and I said, "No, not carers, just the people what's got the learning difficulty", I said "otherwise they're not going to talk". So no carers. They talked about different things, they want more money to go to day centres.

Reflections on Life Now

Work

I had a job for a little while but I find outside work difficult. I don't think they understand really. I've had so much trouble with them I said I wouldn't work again. I just said I wouldn't do it again, I won't work, so I haven't worked since. I'm quite happy doing what I do.

Skills

At Isabel's there was too many to learn. I've learnt to do quite a lot with Isabel because of the cooking and that but I think because there's so many you don't get enough attention. It's just you might as well be back in the hospital. I think the smaller places are much better because I think the carer can help a bit more and she can teach you to do the things that you want, you should be able to do.

I can't fill in the forms yet. Mind you I'm going to the class and they're teaching me. I never learnt to read or write but I'm learning now. I think they should take people who've got learning difficulties in the proper school. I think they are starting to do that now.

Self advocacy

I think being in a group teaches you you've got to learn to say what you want to say and not what everybody else wants you to say. The others feel the same. We've stopped the children, for starts. We've stopped them calling us names, the children don't do it so much. They used to call us horrible names, some of the names you would never dream of. They stopped it, even in Purley, and the teachers go with them now.

There's a little Down's syndrome boy, he comes off the bus to go home because he lives in Purley. And the children would not leave him alone, they used to tease him and everything, and he used to sit on the floor. They called him names, and they squirted water out of the window at me a few times and threw tins but they don't do it any more. That's because I told Keith and he said, "Well, we'll write to the schools".

It stops the children but then you don't stop the adults because they never learn. One Saturday I was with one of my friends and one of the women was so rude my friend was really shocked. This woman said, "Bloody well get out of the way!" My friend was really shocked. It really did upset her because she said, "You know, you have told me about it, that people are rude but I had to believe it to listen to it". She had said, "I'll come with you just to find out, to see what it's like". And she said, "It's damn disgusting that people ought to be allowed to do that".

I'm more confident since I've been in the People First group. You do what you want to do and not get anybody else to do something for you.

I'm chairperson, but it's just the same as anybody else. You just help the people what can't do it for themselves.

Living in the Community

It's hard for the ones what live out on their own mostly, the ones what have the flats. They do miss out. I think they get a bit frightened. Living out in the community, a lot of it, even for me, was new when I first started, so how must they feel? For people what's lived in the hospital for so many years, and then expect them to live on their own, it's wrong. If they've lived with their parents and that, and they go into a flat and they have a little support, they're OK. But for somebody what's lived in a hospital all their life and then to come out and go into a flat, that's murder. To me that is murder because that's just like putting somebody out in the street. They put them out on their own in a house, or by themselves in a flat, and they can't cope with it. I wouldn't do it, and I don't see why anybody else what's been in a long-stay hospital has to do it.

If they lived with their mum, OK, because their mum could watch over them. But if they come out of a big institution like I have, or a few of the others, they are not going to be able to do it. Because they've always had it, they've always had somebody there. They need support and somebody to teach them to do the things they should be able to do. To put them in a flat is murder. And you could find them dead one day, and then say, "Oh, why, how, did it happen?" Because somebody put them in a flat by themself and they've never been used to it. To live on one's own it's cruel. They shouldn't put people what's been in a long stay hospital on their own. I think that's the worst cruelty ever.

I've been taught to cook and everything because the places I've been in they've taught me how to do that. But if I had to go into a flat and pay all the bills and what-have-you it would worry me to death, and I think it would worry anybody else as well. I don't think they should do it. I think I would worry just a little bit for the bills and that because I wouldn't know what to do. I quite like where I am, I think I'll stay for a little while. I don't want a flat, I think it would frighten me. I think it would upset me, and the least little thing upsets me.

A lot of people might not like it, some of them not at all, but I'm quite happy as I am.

Notes

1. The rest of the hospital has subsequently been demolished. Mabel was guest of honour at the party held to mark the end of its life.

Chapter 3

Using Oral Histories

Rebecca Fido and Maggie Potts.[1]

Summary

In this chapter, Rebecca Fido and Maggie Potts examine the ways in which oral history can be used to enrich our understanding of life in an institution during the twentieth century. After discussing their general approach to collecting and using oral histories, Fido and Potts demonstrate the advantages of mixing oral and documentary sources while constructing the history of life in a particular institution. We hope that their account stimulates practitioners to use their expertise and involvement to explore the use of oral histories themselves.

Introduction

With some exceptions, academic histories of both learning disabilities and mental illness have tended to focus on institutions and legislation and have rarely used the memories and experiences of residents themselves. As the age of these large institutions seems to be drawing to an end, the memories of those who were certified under the 1913 Mental Deficiency Act and who have experienced life in these places first-hand are a valuable source of historical information.

Several years ago, we became involved in a project to record the memories and experiences of a small sample of the oldest residents and ex-residents of one particular hospital. We interviewed nine women and eight men, most of whom were admitted to the institution in the 1920s, 1930s or 1940s as children or young adults. The full results of the project were published in detail some years ago in our book 'A Fit Person to be Removed'[2]. In this chapter, we want both to give a general outline of the methods and sources that we used in the preparation of that book and to illustrate precisely how oral history can contribute to writing the history of a particular institution.

Methods

Until recently people with learning disabilities were considered not to be able to speak for themselves, generally because they were thought to be unreliable when they attempted to do so. As a result, people with learning disabilities have remained shut out of, and ignored by, mainstream society. With the present policy of community care, more effort is being made to consider and value the viewpoint of people with a learning disability.

Although there are specific difficulties in obtaining information directly from this population, a number of authors have suggested ways to minimise these difficulties.[3] To a certain extent, the nature of our work required that most interviewees were verbally articulate, but we were able to include three people with severe speech difficulties with the interpretive help of their friends who were also involved in the project. These people and two of the others also had severe physical handicaps and through these interviews we have been able to represent more fully the experiences of people classified previously as 'low grade'.

In addition to interviewing residents, we also gained information from the hospitals extensive archives. Material from these records was useful in a number of ways. First, information from the archives was used (together with memories, anecdotes from other interviewees including ex-staff, and a number of old photographs) as a prompt for recall. Second, this information was used to corroborate memories and identify which era people were discussing when this was not clear. Interviewers were able to help people by asking if the events in question occurred before or after certain landmarks in the institution's history such as new buildings or the presence of World War II soldiers. Finally, and perhaps most importantly, archival records enabled us to determine precisely how, and in what circumstances, information recorded in official documents contrasted with the reality of people's experience. In this way, we could construct a history that included both 'objective' historical records and 'subjective' personal recollections.

The interviews with residents were semi-structured and flexible, giving interviewers a guideline to cover the following areas: people's lives before institutionalisation; their first impressions; the daily routine; work; leisure; special events; rewards and punishments; relationships; changes in conditions; and leaving the institution. Since the interviews required the recollection of very personal and often traumatic events, we attempted to make interviews as informal and conversational as possible. Questions were simply worded and could be rephrased if interviewees had problems understanding them. Interviewees were assured throughout that they would not be identified.

Since it has been noted that people with a learning disability have a tendency to conform to other people's expectations, there was a danger that interviewees would respond in line with the interviewers' perspective rather than their own. This was minimised by using open-ended questions which potentially would also yield fuller responses. Although some research indicates that people with learning disabilities do not always respond well to open-ended questions,[4] this approach appeared to work well in this case, perhaps because most of the respondents in this study were amongst the more able. Most were able to give full and detailed accounts, appearing to speak their minds even when clearly contrary to the interviewer's expectations. Overall, every one of the interviews yielded useful and interesting information about institutional life.

Because we were novices at historical research, we had a great deal to learn about transcribing and collating information efficiently and systematically. For the purpose of writing-up, we decided to organize all the material into different subject areas in much the same way as the interviews were to be structured.

However, in being flexible, the interviews naturally could not always follow that sequence or stick to one area at a given time. Only as we began to sort out the material for writing up did it become apparent that it was necessary to transcribe the interviews accordingly. This we did automatically with subsequent interviews. Following this, we also put together all the interviewees' comments on each of the different topics with cross references where necessary. Information from institutional records and other documents were arranged in a similar way.

In writing up the interviews for publication, we felt that it was important to protect the confidentiality and anonymity of the interviewees, particularly since many of their recollections contained some very personal and possibly controversial material. The names of the contributors, as well the names of the institution, its annexes and local districts, were therefore changed. We also considered it important to gain informed consent from our interviewees. Thus, a simply worded consent form, which indicated that people understood the purpose of the interviews and agreed to have their memories published, was signed by name or mark and witnessed.

Since none of the interviewees could read fluently, but because we felt that it was important to give them the opportunity of hearing how the work was being put together, we decided to hold readings of the work. A tape-recording was made for those who could not attend. Although we had initially decided to leave people's real names in the text to enable them to recognize themselves, we eventually decided to let people pick their own pseudonyms if they wished. Presenting the work with pseudonyms reassured people further that they would not be identified even amongst themselves.

During the project, three people died, underlining the importance of doing this research now. Unfortunately, these people did not get the chance to listen to and comment on the historical account that resulted.

Personal accounts of life in an institution

Wide scale institutionalisation of people with what we now refer to as learning disabilities was initiated by the Mental Deficiency Act of 1913. At around the turn of this century, industrialization and social Darwinism both contributed to a strong campaign that called for urgent measures to deal with problems of 'mental deficiency'. Underlying this was the belief that 'mental defectives' were not only the cause of most social evils but were an economic burden:

The feebleminded are a parasitic, predatory class, never
capable of self-support or of managing their own affairs.
(....) We have only begun to understand the importance of
feeblemindedness as a factor in the causation of pauperism,
crime and other social problems. (....) Every feebleminded
person, especially the highgrade imbecile, is a potential
criminal, needing only the proper environment and opportunity for
the development and expression of his criminal tendencies. The
unrecognized imbecile is a most dangerous element in the
community.[5]

Life-long institutionalisation for most, if not all, 'mental defectives'
both for 'their own protection and the protection of others' became an
energetic crusade. The Mental Deficiency Act of 1913, the first truly
effective legislation in this field, required local authorities to certify all
'mental defectives' and set up special certified institutions.

The institution featured in this study was set up in 1919 as a 'Colony
for Mental Defectives', the colonization of so-called 'inferior peoples'
being an already well established and popular British policy at this
time. Colonies were said to be more humane and efficient than the old
one-block asylums and institutions. With the ultimate aim of maximum
self-sufficiency, colonies were based on a village layout with a central
administration block surrounded by pavilion homes (later known as
villas) and various amenities such as workshops, a school, a recreation
hall and a farm. For the local authority, there was the advantage of
allowing the addition of buildings as funds became available.
Consequently, as the institution grew, it became increasingly insular
and cut off from the community.

The strict hierarchy of both staff and patients was sharply reflected in
the nature of the accommodation provided, from the Medical
Superintendent's large 4-bedroomed house to the homes for the 'lowest
grade' patients. These latter homes were positioned well away from the
main entrances and other villas, reflecting the shame associated with
such severe disabilities. For cost effectiveness, villas were not to be too
small, but they were also not to be so large (that is, not over 60 patients)
that they destroyed 'an impression of homeliness'!

One of the main motives for institutionalisation in the early decades of
this century was an overriding fear that the 'feebleminded' would
'repeat their type' resulting in the 'propagation of a degenerate stock'.
There was particular concern about young women referred to as 'high

Archive pictures from 'The Park' c. 1940-1950

and medium grade' who were presumed to be more immoral and fertile than other women. In this particular locality (and probably elsewhere too), this prejudice was clearly reflected in the greater priority given to providing accommodation for young women, with the first institution to be set up being a Girl's Training Home. As residents pointed out, all but the most severely disabled adult males and females were housed on separate sides of the site as an inbuilt precaution against mixing:

> We weren't allowed to talk to any boys. We wasn't allowed to sit with them in 'recreation hall'. Boys had to be at one side and girls at the other.

Under the Mental Deficiency Act of 1913, the first step to detainment was certification. This involved the assessment of people according to three levels of defect. From the lowest to the highest 'grade', a person thought to be 'mentally defective' was officially labelled as an 'idiot', an 'imbecile' or a 'feeble-minded person'. There was an additional catch-all category, 'moral defective'. The authorities believed that people referred to as 'high grade' were the 'real social menace'. Thus, under the 'moral defective' clause many people, often adolescents, who would not now be considered as having any disability were detained after committing minor offences such as petty theft or, like one of our respondents, for having an illegitimate baby.

The interviewees remembered some aspects of the traumatic certification and admission procedure better than others. For instance, none of the residents interviewed spontaneously mentioned the medical and judicial assessments. When asked specifically about them, people either could not recall them at all or could do so only very vaguely. However most of the people we interviewed could remember life before institutionalisation and could also recall many of the events leading to admission.

Of particular significance to our respondents, was the role of Mr. Grey, the local Mental Deficiency Committee's Executive Officer, the man who supervised the whole procedure, from ascertainment to admission. Despite the advice given in an Officer's hand book that 'All Officers must establish a friendly and sympathetic bond with patients', this man is closely identified with the fear and anger that the procedure caused:

> Grey! Oh blow that bloomin' thing! I used to go running to me mother. Mind you, they used to come down that street and make you come out of the door. Ooh, I hated him! He wouldn't let anybody

live. He did a lot of damage, picking people up what didn't deserve
to be picked up. He weren't only after me. He were clever. He got
hold of nice girls in there, just like me.

Some people's memories of admission to the Colony vividly recapture
the fear, bewilderment and helplessness most people, at whatever level
of comprehension, must have felt on being 'put away' in such a large,
depersonalizing place:

My grandfather didn't say where I was going. That's what
got me, he didn't say where. Frightened I were. I felt awful! I
wanted to go back out. I felt upset! I couldn't stick it in here!

However, some found it harder to recall and articulate their feelings not
just in relation to admission but more generally. In commenting on
painful experiences and various deprivations such as the lack of personal
possessions, birthday celebrations, friendships or visits from relatives,
people would sometimes say, 'I didn't bother'. Inherent difficulties in
interpreting and describing feelings may well have been compounded
by the fact that institutions do not encourage or expect inmates to need
to do so. Pretending not to feel or not to mind must, for some, become
an automatic and effective method of coping with the pain of neglect.
Having interviewers who were well known and trusted by the individual
respondents helped to some extent, as did including specific questions
about people's feelings. It was also useful to listen to the ways in which
things were said as well as what was said, though this can be susceptible
to biased interpretation.

The institutional system exercised complete control and tyranny over the
inmates through reward and punishment. Work pay/pocket money,
visits to and from home, holidays and recreational activities were
considered privileges that had to be earned by 'good conduct and work',
as one resident remembers:

Patients had to be careful how they behaved in their work and
the villa or wherever they were 'cos there was strict staff in those
days and any offence, they used to be up before one of the senior
doctors. In the case of first offences, they were warned of the
serious nature of the offence and what would happen if that or
anything like it was repeated. Then they were placed before the
doctor and they lost all their privileges for a certain length of time.
As far as privileges were concerned, used to be going to films and
concerts and in hospital grounds, recreation hall and money included.

More severe punishments, both official and unofficial, such as cold baths, scrubbing, carrying bags of sand and beatings, existed for those who more openly rebelled against the system. All the villas had special side-rooms for punishment and there were punishment villas in the male, female, and children's sections of the Colony. We found that some of the respondents, especially in the initial interviews, denied being punished or giving cause to be punished, finding it easier to describe what happened to other people:

> If you got caught doing summat to a girl they used to lock you up in a sideroom. They used to run away did some of them and they had to bring 'em back and put 'em in a sideroom. And scrubbing used to have shorts on. Same wi' girls. They used to 'same on 'female side. We used to go round and see girls just in their knickers scrubbing floors. Villa 8 used to be their locking up villa. Locked up in side rooms without no clothes on.

One or two people were reluctant even to talk about this topic, perhaps not wishing to appear too critical of the institution. One woman who has lived in the hospital since she was six had a generally uncritical and positive outlook, past and present, in the first interview. Only in later interviews,[6] one of which was conducted with another interviewee who had become very embittered, did she remember the darker side of institutional life:

> You know if we did something wrong we had to be in us nighties all day and be punished. Couldn't go out anywhere, couldn't have your visitors to see you.

> If you were bursting to go somewhere and you wet yourself, you know like with me, you got punished. Say you were in a wheelchair and you couldn't talk to tell them, you still got punished!

> I didn't like it (food) and we used to grumble and groan. But if we didn't eat it for your tea, they'd save it for your supper. You had to eat it and eat it and eat it 'til it were gone! We daren't leave anything, them days. We daren't even say to staff, 'I don't want this.' You daren't be rude!

Despite this woman's apparent satisfaction with life and improvements in the system, she could eventually admit that she felt that she had lived in the institution too long once she became more secure and confident:

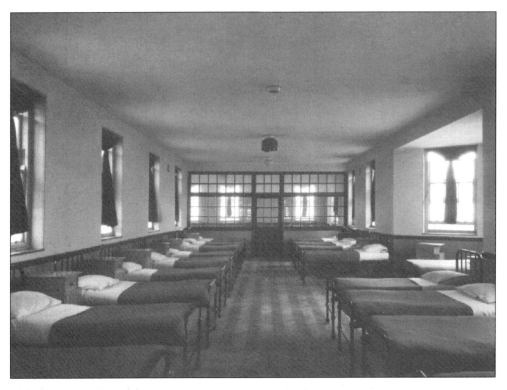

Archive pictures from 'The Park' c. 1940-1950

Now I've started going home, I'm a lot happier. I never used to go home or anything. It was alright then (in the old days). I think it was nice and alright. I hadn't been here long enough then, but now I'm thinking I've been at The Park too long now. I wish I could leave in one way. I don't mean to be nasty. I'd like to go and see somewhere, you know, nice places. Would they let us have a change? I'm just getting a bit fed up of being here. You know I've been here a long time. Are they supposed to be building some houses? I hope I'm not going to stay here much longer!

Conclusion

In this chapter, we have explored precisely how oral histories can be collected from people with learning disabilities and given some indication of the ways in which such personal recollections can complement, and often challenge, historical accounts based on documentary sources. In attempting to include and inform contributors of the progress that we were making throughout the project, we became concerned about people's responses to becoming more aware of the extent to which their treatment was prejudiced and unfair. In some ways, though, we (the researchers) appeared more overtly horrified by the material than did the residents that we interviewed. Having suffered a lifetime of being downgraded and discriminated against, the contributors' immediate response was in fact to be encouraged at having their experience recognized.

Encouragingly, the interviewees' reactions to the work also indicate that it does accurately reflect their experience at the hands of the authorities. All seemed pleased to have their memories and thoughts taken seriously. And in recognizing the injustice done to them in the past, they remain keen to give us their view of this history:

I'd just like people to know so they can realize what it was we'd had to go through. It's not true what was written down! They did it just to keep us locked up, so that people would think we're mental!

Notes

1. This paper first appeared as Rebecca Fido and Maggie Potts, "'It's not true what was written down!": experiences of life in a mental handicap institution', *Oral History*, 17, (1989), 31-4. That earlier version has been slightly modified for inclusion in this collection.

2. Maggie Potts and Rebecca Fido, '*A Fit Person to be Removed': Personal Accounts of Life in a Mental Deficiency Institution*, (Northcote House, 1991).

3. M. C. Flynn, 'Adults who are Mentally Handicapped as Consumers: Issues and Guidelines for Interviewing', *Journal of Mental Deficiency Research*, 30, (1986), 369-377; C. K. Seligman, E. C. Budd, J. L. Winer, C.J. Schoenrock and P.W. Martin, 'Evaluating alternative techniques of questioning mentally retarded persons', *American Journal of Mental Deficiency*, 86, (1982).

4. Seligman et al., 'Evaluating alternative techniques'.

5. Quoted in S. B. Sarason and J. Doris, *Psychological Problems in Mental Deficiency*, (4th edition, New York, Harper and Row, 1969).

6. As well as enabling people to feel more at ease and to disclose further information, re-interviewing also allowed us to follow up points or ask about things that were not initially inquired about.

Chapter 4

Recording the History of an Institution:
The Royal Eastern Counties Institution at Colchester[1]

Andrew Stevens

Summary

In this chapter, Andy Stevens examines some of the methods involved in recording institutional histories. By focusing in particular on the history of the Royal Eastern Counties Institution in Colchester, particularly during the interwar years, he explores in detail the availability of sources for institutional histories, the ways in which those sources can be interpreted, and some of the insights into institutional life that can be gathered from close scrutiny of a variety of written records and oral sources.

Introduction

The Eastern Counties Asylum for Idiots and Imbeciles was established in 1859 at Essex Hall in Colchester, Essex, the first regional idiot asylum in this country. Essex Hall itself had originally been built as a railway hotel and, prior to its opening as the Eastern Counties Asylum, had operated as an annexe of the Metropolitan Society for Idiots and Imbeciles.[2] In 1914, the Asylum was renamed the Royal Eastern Counties Institution and, before becoming a hospital under the National Health Service, it had been independent, rather than local authority managed, and most administrative records remained in the locality. Unfortunately, when the site was recently destroyed, most of the documentary evidence was destroyed with it or has subsequently been mislaid.[3]

The documentary evidence currently available at the remaining annexe of the hospital mainly consists of incomplete admissions and discharge registers and patient records. No significant hospital documents remain in the local record office, other than the annual reports to subscribers. It would appear that little archival material was passed on by the hospital. However, it would have been difficult for archivists to assess the significance of material from the Institution when there were few published histories of such hospitals.

Institutional histories can be undertaken for a variety of purposes: for academic historical research; to assist the rehabilitation of patients; as part of a campaign for, or against, closure; or as a public relations exercise by the health service agency using the site. Each approach will tend to utilise different sources and emphasize different aspects of institutional life. In this chapter, I want to argue that a variety of sources both from the institution and from elsewhere need to be interpreted carefully in order to build up a complete picture of life in an institution during the twentieth century.

Sources

In researching the history of a particular institution, it is tempting to base the study exclusively on surviving written sources. In some cases, unlike the Eastern Counties Institution, there is a surprisingly rich source of written administrative records still available, including admission/discharge books; villa or ward nurse duty books; doctors and visitors' books; patient records; and general archives.

Unfortunately, although it was the largest independent voluntary mental deficiency institution operating in the inter-war period, remaining documentary evidence from the Royal Eastern Counties Institution is relatively limited. However, some registers survive from certain periods. Although these are rich sources of statistical information, changes in recording make comparison over time difficult, particularly with regard to boarded-out patients. Early patient records still exist for patients whose death was noted. However, these records refer mainly to discharged patients and are, therefore, generally restricted to relatively 'high grade' patients. The records are also restricted by the fact that nurses did not have access to files before the National Health Service and contact with doctors prior to this was limited. Files do, however, usefully indicate the post-war introduction of personal record systems of assessment and treatment. A further major gap in the documentary evidence is the absence of any ward record books, which provided a daily nursing record for each ward or villa.

The lack of substantial institutional records often makes it necessary to exploit a variety of alternative sources, including official government sources, the published annual reports of institutions and their parent societies, contemporary books, journals and newspapers, and oral histories. Let me consider each of these in turn.

Central Government Reports
Published official sources, such as central government committee reports, can offer useful comparative (albeit sometimes limited) information about mental deficiency institutions, about local authority ascertainment rates, and about other contemporary planning and operational issues.[4] There have been a number of published policy committee reports (such as the Report of the Royal Commission on the Care and Control of the Feeble-Minded of 1908, the Wood Report of 1928, and the Brock Report of 1934). The Board of Control, which had overall responsibility for the administration of mental deficiency services, also produced annual reports from its creation in 1914 until 1947, after which time many institutions became part of the National Health Service. These reports mention individual institutions on an intermittent basis.

Public Records at the Public Record Office provide access to other material including some Board of Control work after 1945, but a very limited number of records have been selected for preservation, and files on policy issues only occasionally have detailed information on individual institutions or hospitals. More detailed information is, however, available where a hospital has been subject to a public enquiry, such as at Ely or South

Ockendon. The Hansard reports of proceedings in parliamentary sessions also mention incidents at specific hospitals, particularly in the 1950s during the campaigns to repeal the Mental Deficiency Acts.

Local Government Records

Local government records can also be useful. The committee reports of local boards for education, mental deficiency committees, poor law guardians and public health officers often contain local records of services. Where these are available, they can provide helpful background information about local services although they tend to focus on local authority managed services more than on the provision of other voluntary services in the area. However, a wider search of local government records may yield further information, for example, on the planning and construction of buildings and on financial issues.

Annual Reports from Institutions

Independent institutions also published annual reports for sub-scribers which, although they may reflect official biases, are often quite detailed. Independent hospitals usually received most of their income through poor law or local authority patient fees, but also retained a large network of charitable subscribers and fund raisers. The institution would therefore publish an annual account of the developments in services, events and financial accounts. These publications were written to encourage fund raising, but contain details of official history which is either unavailable elsewhere or which can confirm information from other sources. The annual reports from the Royal Eastern Counties Institution, for example, contain lengthy reports from the superintendent and extracts from Board of Control inspections which are no longer available from Government records. However, historical accounts based primarily on these reports will necessarily ignore the perspectives of patients and staff.

Other written material

Other sources such as books, journals and local and national newspapers are less likely to contain information on individual institutions, particularly before the hospital scandals of the 1960's. It would appear that issues related to institutions for people with learning disabilities were afforded less coverage than those related to other health care institutions, in both medical journals and local media.

A wide search of contemporary professional journals, particularly medical and public health journals, can reveal descriptions of methods of treatment at individual institutions. The main textbooks, such as Alfred

Tredgold's *Mental Deficiency* (which was first published in 1908 and which remained the main reference work for the first half of this century), deal mostly with general medical issues, although they do sometimes make reference to work at particular institutions.[5] Tredgold, for example, not only discussed the work of prominent medical superintendents, but also published medical and other photographs of patients at these institutions. It should be remembered, however, that medical journals and books provide primarily a medical perspective, providing very little information about the lives of patients or those looking after them. Non-medical publications and other written sources are often difficult to find. Recollections of nurses, social workers and patients have subsequently been written and published, but contemporary material for the inter-war years is rare.

Oral History
There is another source of information which affords yet another perspective, that is oral history. Patients or survivors of institutional treatment, retired doctors, nurses and staff are often willing to talk about their experiences of institutional life. Interviews with patients, nurses, other staff and relatives allow one to build up an understanding of daily life (such as the impact of the institution on the lives of those living and working within it) that cannot be gained from documentary sources. Even medical officers will have different perspectives from the superintendents, who tend to write most of the published material. The earliest recollections from the Royal Eastern Counties Institution interviews that I have obtained so far refer to the period around the First World War.

It is important to be prepared properly before undertaking oral history research. Taped interviews for historical research are useful records in themselves, but it is important to consider issues such as interviewer training, question schedules, technical equipment, confidentiality, copyright, transcriptions and archiving of results, before rather than during the research. Information can be obtained on these issues from the National Sound Archive in London, and there are useful publications on oral history techniques.[6]

Interpretation of the sources
The appropriate selection of information is one of the major difficulties facing anyone interested in historical research. Most people undertaking research into the history of institutions for people with learning disability will have limited time, either due to the imminent closure of a hospital, or because they are working on the material on a part-time basis. Many researchers currently engaged in constructing the history

of institutions have had difficulty reducing the material to a publishable form. The most successful are those who adopt a restricted perspective, focusing exclusively on patients' stories, for example.[7] Archivists are also faced with a similar position when selecting material for preservation. There are few general commentaries on the history of institutions to guide either historians or archivists. In addition, previous works reflect the bias of over-reliance on public written sources or derive their perspective exclusively from the campaigning zeal of welfare professionals and self advocates since the early 1980s.[8]

These latter works often contain a number of assumptions about institutions that need to be challenged. Such assumptions include beliefs: that institutions were only places of incarceration and exploitation; that mental deficiency institutions were like asylums, but with different patients; that all large institutions operated similar regimes; that the importance of educative functions at institutions declined from the late nineteenth century; that doctors ran institutions, nurses controlled patients and patients were 'passive' victims of the staff; and that conditions within institutions were bad and got better after the Second World War.

There are clearly problems with these assumptions and the sources on which they are based. For example, to view mental deficiency institutions as a single organisational form makes the interpretation of any qualitative information about the life within such institutions difficult. Any interviewer or researcher should be sensitive to variations between institutions, variations which are often not clear from either published general histories or individual accounts of life in the institutions.

Unfortunately, there is, so far, very little comparative material available to explore these variations. In reality, there was a wide variation in the size, organisational structure, and the care and treatment regimes of different institutions. National legislative changes such as the 1913 Mental Deficiency Act, the National Health Service Act of 1946, and the 1959 Mental Health Act certainly had impacts on all institutions, but these impacts were not uniform. The size, status and location of the institution will have influenced how legislative change or national policies affected individual regimes.

The introduction of new forms of residential care, such as the village settlement movement after the Second World War, also have relevance to an understanding of pre-war institutions. RESCARE and associated village residential organisations have recently claimed affinity with the old mental deficiency institutions. Despite reservations about the oversimplistic revisionist history of such institutions offered by their supporters, the post-war development of village settlements in Britain can perhaps be seen as an evolution from the colony concept as much as a derivative of the philosophy of Rudolf Steiner. This is particularly evident when comparisons are made with the larger independent institutions which retained pedagogic influences in their treatment regimes.[9]

Towards a more sensitive history of institutions

Institutions for people with learning disabilities have clearly differed in a number of significant ways. One way to develop a more sensitive account of the history of institutions (and one more amenable to comparative analysis) might be, firstly, to classify institutions according to those differences and then to explore their development and their facilities within each of the categories.

In this section, I shall examine the histories of institutions in terms of their legal status, their architectural structure, and their organisational regimes.

Legal status

Under the 1913 Mental Deficiency Act, institutions were classified as follows:

> State Institutions (s.35)
> Local Authority and Voluntary (s.36)
> Public (Poor Law) Premises (s.37)
> Certified Houses (s.49)
> Approved Homes (s.50)

Local authority and voluntary institutions (s.36) accounted for the majority of growth in institutional placements during the inter-war period. Local authority and large poor law institutions tended to reflect the views of their administrations and were often of a rational, low cost, municipal style brick architecture. Calderstones, originally designed as a mental asylum for Lancashire County Council, started operating in 1921 with a planned provision for 2,000 people. Other local authorities used small hostels or independent institutions. The most prominent of these independent institutions were the original large idiot asylums established prior to the 1913 Mental Deficiency Act. Most of these had started as adaptations of large private houses and had subsequently built adjacent annexes or acquired other sites. The Royal Eastern Counties Institution, for example, had been a railway hotel and started in 1859 with accommodation for only 60 'pupils', although it rapidly expanded. As will become apparent later, the nature of the accommodation influenced organisational regimes. Although they struggled with their architectural expansion, such large institutions remained significant suppliers of services during the inter-war years.

Certified houses also dramatically varied in size, from small private homes for a few children, such as Avonhurst, to larger institutions such as the Normansfield Training Institution in Middlesex, which became a National Health Service hospital. The respective regimes of Margaret McDowell and Dr. Langdon Down at these institutions were also significantly different.

Architectural structure

Institutions can also be classified and analysed according to the organisation of their buildings. Although an awareness of the social impact of mental deficiency institutions cannot be primarily based on analysis of physical environments, such an analysis can nevertheless contribute to an understanding of institutional life.

Given the limited preservation of material relevant to individual institutions, this simple analysis can be a useful comparative tool over time and between institutions. Old ordnance survey maps will be available for most institutional sites subsequently demolished. Such maps can be used not only to deduce some of the functions of the buildings and, there-fore, to clarify institutional regimes, but also to serve as a tool to trigger the memories of older patients and retired staff.

One of the first English classifications of lunatic and idiot asylums was made on this architectural basis, emphasising the ward arrange-ments for the provision of light and air circulation. In 1891, H.C.Burdett described four main classes of institutions:

> Pavilion H
> Block H
> Corridor
> Composite or Heap of Buildings.

Unfortunately all three idiot asylums that Burdett examined (the Eastern Counties Asylum, the Royal Albert Asylum, and Earlswood) were in the last category. However, the arrangements of buildings can be a useful interpretative study in some cases. Andrew Scull drew on this material for understanding nineteenth century attitudes to insanity. Wolfensberger used architectural studies of institutions in the United States in a similar way, but also included building materials and internal decoration in his discussion.[10]

Large purpose-built mental deficiency institutions (except the Metropolitan Asylums Board institutions), are essentially a twentieth-century organisational form, but were constructed along the same lines as poor law lunatic asylums. They were essentially rationalist constructions, with the primary functions of low cost and sexual segregation made evident in the architectural construction and floor plans.

The concept of a 'colony system' (a concept that informed the construction of many institutions around the turn of the twentieth century) was also noted by Burdett, who described a colony as:

> situated at some distance from the main building and
> devoted to those patients who are more reliable and able to enjoy
> the comparative freedom found there. These colonies are really
> farm settlements, but in addition to the merely agricultural labour;
> of which they are the centre; the work shops are often attached to
> them[11].

However, the experience of patients within institutions has not been mainly located in such colonies. Many of the major institutions were not purpose-built, but adapted and enlarged buildings of an earlier period. Regional variations in the size and location of institutions indicate differences in response by local authorities to the national policies of institutionalization in the early twentieth century.

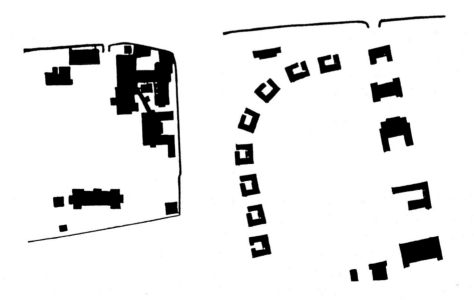

Figure 4.1. Plans of the sites of the two halves of the central institution (from Ordnance Survey): Essex Hall (left) and Turner Village (right)

The two halves of the Eastern Counties main institution (Figure 4.1) illustrate two different architectural arrangements. The original site, Essex Hall (the converted railway hotel), was called the Central Institution. Further buildings on this site were added on a piecemeal basis when funds allowed. The most important of these were the South Suffolk Annexe (1889) and Peckover Technical Schools (1900). The farm buildings were on the opposite side of the road south of the railway line.

This composite site arrangement can be compared with the extension site, Turner Village. The new colony type of institution, opened in 1935, is typical of the period. It was clearly to be the central site of the Royal Eastern Counties Institution. Initially planned in 1915, it had been subject, like many other similar projects of the period, to considerable delay through planning and construction. The overall plan was for the construction of sixteen, mainly 40 bedded villas, laid out in two symmetrical arcs either side of a central spine formed by the administrative block at the head, an assembly hall, staff accommodation, kitchens, laundry and power-house. At the base were the workshops and playing fields. The first eight villas which form the male side were built in the first phase and males from Essex Hall moved in 1935, along with some from Witham. The villas of the female side were never completed due to the advent of the Second World War, and subsequent constructions under the National Health Service administration were of a different plan and of a pre-fabricated form, nicknamed 'aeroplane villas'.

This symmetrical colony plan has strong similarities with the structure of late nineteenth and early twentieth-century institutions, the earliest of which were built by the Metropolitan Asylums Board in the 1870s and 1880s. This form of colony layout also conforms to ideas set out in government reports on the construction of institutions, to the municipal colony buildings of the inter-war period (on which the Royal Eastern Counties Institution extension at Turner Village is based), and to the Camphill Villages of the 1950-60s, all of which demonstrate a trend from large central blocks to more dispersed cottages. The concept of symmetry (initially for male/female segregation) in planning has remained evident in later planned communities. A deeper analysis of the plans of mental deficiency institutions is beyond the scope of this discussion. However, it is worth remembering that, in the experience of nurses at Essex Hall, segregative regimes were less easily imposed in non-purpose built institutions. Large institutional buildings or dispersed cottage-style colonies in themselves impose isolation and affect the quality of life of patients and staff.

Organisational regimes

Organisational regimes are more difficult to classify without detailed analysis of administrative records and oral history sources and without comparisons between institutional regimes. A brief summary of the regime at the Royal Eastern Counties Institution will illustrate the potential of this type of analysis.

Despite the generally central role of the medical superintendent and government guidance on the operation of certified mental deficiency institutions, administration was likely to be varied as a result of variations in size, regional location, and primary funding sources. In addition, variations could be the result of an institution's domination by the personalities of individual medical superintendents (such as Dr. Gill at Calderstones and Dr. Shuttleworth at the Royal Albert Institution) or by a family dynasty (such as Langdon Down at Normansfield). Some of these variables can be seen at the Royal Eastern Counties Institution.

The Asylum became the Royal Eastern Counties Institution in 1914. Dr. Frank Douglas Turner, medical officer since 1904, had been appointed as the first medical superintendent the year before, a position that he had 'inherited' from his father, John Turner. Turner (senior) had been the secretary of the institution under William Millard and had run it since 1889 as superintendent. All his children spent most of their lives in the institution, since he appointed his other son, Arthur Turner, as Secretary and his daughter, Miss Edith Turner, as Head Matron. Miss Edith, Dr. Turner and his wife effectively remained resident at Essex Hall until the end of the Second World War.

Dr. F.D. Turner was a significant influence on the development of the role of medical superintendents in mental deficiency institutions during the inter-war years. He was the only president of the Royal Medico-Psychological Association (later the Royal College of Psychiatrists) to come from a mental deficiency institution and was a major influence on government policy through his work on government committees and national voluntary organisations. Although he wrote no major books, his influence can be noted in committee reports and in a manual for mental deficiency nurses.

By 1930, there was an established pattern to the organisation of activities within the main institution. Interviews conducted in the course of this author's research clearly indicate that this was based on a hierarchy of power which incorporated everyone involved - nurses, doctors and patients. One of the most important features of this structure, however, was the extent to which this was gender related. This can be best illustrated by a chart of status positions - the pecking order of the institution (Figure 4.2).

Patients were a valuable source of labour. The patients identified as 'higher grade' were also responsible for much of the care of the 'lower grades'. Such a classification according to 'grades' was commonly used in institutions and is referred to in most published patients' histories. Differences in the ways in which nursing hierarchies were organized have been less well documented.

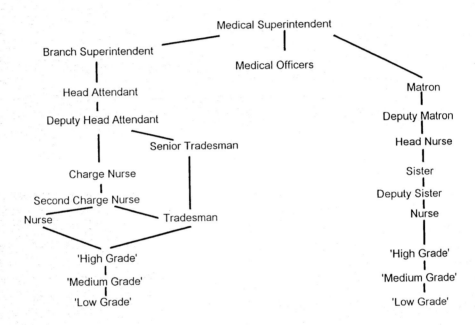

Figure 4.2. Chart of the Perceived Status Hierarchy at the RECI (derived from oral history interviews)

Staff recognized differences between what were known as 'the female side' and 'the male side'. These differences were established before the physical separation of the two 'sides' into different sites in 1935. On the female side there was a recognisable General Nursing Council (GNC) type of nurse ranking. On the male side this was more complex.

The nursing staff and the work supervisory staff had separate areas of responsibility. Some female instructors were part-time staff or sessional staff who were not seen as part of the institution. The male work-related staff were known as tradesmen and had their own ranking system (senior carpenter, second carpenter, and so on). However, they also had to care for the patients in the mornings and evenings. The Senior Tradesman also undertook shift duty as officer-in-charge. He had status as

Male staff at the Institution, circa 1910

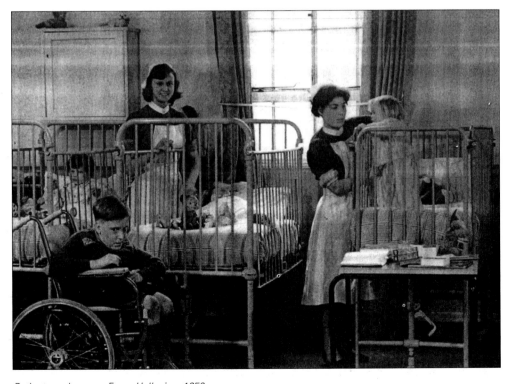

Patients and nurses, Essex Hall, circa 1950

Dr. F. D. Turner, 1948

supervisor of both male nurses and tradesmen and was consulted by Dr. Turner in both capacities. Tradesmen were also allowed to train as Royal Medico-Psychological Association nurses, but many did not bother as their pay was often already higher than that of the nursing staff.

Rank was not so clearly differentiated on the male side as on the female side. The female nurses had a different uniform according to rank, in a similar way to GNC nurses. However, all male staff including charge nurses, tradesmen and nurses wore the same uniform, although senior grades were allowed better quality cloth. Only the Head Attendant displayed a specific sign of rank. He was distinguishable by braid on his cap.

The variation in clothing worn by patients of different grade also performed a similar function to a uniform. The grade of male and female patients could generally be ascertained by normal day clothing, and special clothing was sometimes worn by violent patients or those receiving punishment.

Dr. Turner was particularly keen to maintain direct contact with all staff and patients, which was increasingly difficult as the institution expanded in patient numbers and over different sites. It is evident that authority on the female side was fundamentally patriarchal. This was in part due to the fact that his family in 1930 had maintained apartments in Essex Hall for two generations. Dr. Turner encouraged staff and patients to see him as a father:

Every one of them, patient or staff, must be able to come to you
with their troubles. 'Daddy' is the name I like best to hear.[12]

Turner was often remembered by female nurses as 'the grey haired old
gentleman' who waited up for them when they were returning with an
absconding patient, or who gave out presents at Christmas. Miss Edith
was remembered with affection by female nurses, but where she tried to
adopt a similar matriarchal role she had less success. Other nurses com-
plained that she was fussy and she was nicknamed 'Rubberneck'.

In contrast, the male side was run in a more rationalist and military
manner, akin to prison authority. Respect arose from an ability to do the
job. Male nurses were generally more active in the union and were more
cynical about the Turner family.

> The pay structure, I think six pounds a week for a charge
> nurse then - Dr Turner was dumbfounded that the money
> had to be coughed up. He didn't think the staff were worth that
> type of money... (Miss Edith) was useless. She couldn't thread a
> needle. And she'd be oh, over six foot, with a big reddish
> dress, a damn big starched hat and she couldn't take a
> temperature - no qualifications. (From interview with a male nurse.)

There was a similar differentiation by gender in attitudes to care. It is
beyond the scope of this paper to offer a detailed examination on this
subject but I shall briefly mention differences in two following areas: work
and regulation of behaviour.

Patient allocation to areas of work seemed to be arbitrary, but 'high
grade' patients usually had better jobs, which gave higher pocket
money and a degree of independence. Male jobs included the farm, mat
shop and boot shop; female jobs included the laundry, domestic work,
and caring for the 'low grades'. One of the highest status male patients
was the bricklayer's mate. On the female side, the highest status
patients would be matron's maids, but the 'higher grade' women known
as 'working girls' were sometimes afforded a status almost equivalent
to staff. Many worked as domestics outside the institution and might
live at an annex, Lexden House, while others nursed the 'low grades'.
They earned respect from nurses by the quality of care they gave.

> Where you might get a nurse taking to a - somebody - because they
> looked pretty or looked a like a little angel, you'd, you'd get these
> girls - you know some of them had a great deal of deformity. You'd

get them saying 'There's my friend' you know and that was lovely.
They showed you, you know -
Interviewer - How to, how to do it?
Yes, yes they did. (From interview with female nurse.)

Control was exercised within the institution in a variety of ways.
Segregation of the sexes, strict timetables and routines, and punishment
dress were similar to those in other institutions. From the interviews,
violence and segregation did not appear to be as strong a feature of control
on the female side. There was only one small room, in a tower of Essex
Hall, available for segregating women and that was not often used.
Violence to patients beyond simple restraint was not condoned by most
nurses. Only one significant event was recalled during this period.
When two nurses locked a patient in a bathroom and gave her the 'wet
towel treatment', they were ostracised by their colleagues. Similarly,
patients were often 'sent to Coventry' if they assaulted a nurse.

On the male side, violence by patients to nurses and vice versa was
more common. Turner Village was built with one villa of different
shape to the others - Villa 8. This had a pair of isolation rooms in
each wing. It was known as the punishment villa. Patients won status
among their peers on the male side if they had a period of residence on
either Villa 8 or had been to Rampton State Institution. Each villa had
a different class of patients depending on their grade, job and behaviour.
Villa 1 patients had highest formal status, but Villa 8 also afforded
informal high status. Many of the patients there were also 'high grade'
and devised ingenious methods of escape.

Sexual behaviour was also carefully regulated. Identifying all patients
as 'girls' and 'boys' constituted, on one level, a denial of the right to
adult relationships - although these did develop despite the difficulties
of institutional life. Sexual segregation was supposed to discourage
heterosexual relationships in the institution for nurses as well as
patients. Christmas and dances were the only formal point of contact
between female and male patients. There are numerous stories of
patients making the best of this opportunity. Similar stories exist for
other institutions. Attitudes to sexual controls were also different on
each side of the institution with regard to same-sex relationships. It
appears from the oral histories that sexual activity between male
patients was more common than between female patients. Staff were
more concerned about the threat of serious assault on the male side and
may have condoned or possibly encouraged same sex relationships as a
way of reducing the risk of assault to staff. (One member of staff was

isolated on the villa at night.) By contrast, potential lesbian relationships were vehemently discouraged. Girls who were observed to be
'over-friendly' were separated into different wards or even transferred
to another branch.

Conclusion

In this chapter, I have surveyed some of the various sources that need
to be analysed in the process of recording the history of an institution.
There are clearly similarities between the information from interviews
and documentary sources relating to the operation of the Royal Eastern
Counties Institution and other published histories. However, my
research at the Royal Eastern Counties Institution challenges some of
the assumptions generally made about the regimes of mental deficiency
institutions before the war. In particular, it indicates that there were
both variations in the ways institutions have operated and differences in
regimes across sites. I would therefore argue that in order to understand the provision of services under the Mental Deficiency Acts, it is
necessary to reconstruct the operation of a range of individual institutions
using as wide a range of sources as possible.

Notes

1. This chapter is based on material collected during continuing PhD research on the Royal Eastern Counties Institution by the author at the University of Essex.

2. For an early account of the asylum's history, see W. Millard, *The Idiot and his Helpers: A Brief History of the Essex Hall, Earlswood, and other Asylums in England and Scotland for the Idiot and Imbecile*, (London, 1864).

3. Tellingly, public protests against the destruction of the institution in order to make way for a housing estate focused on its importance as a Victorian railway hotel designed by Cubitt rather than on the fact that it was the oldest site for continual use as an institution for people with learning disabilities.

4. Large municipal and university libraries will keep copies of Hansard and other government reports. Annual Reports of the Board of Control were not all published but available editions can be found at the British (Reference) Library. 'ED' and 'MH' files at the Public Record Office at Kew are also useful. Local records offices hold varying amounts of local authority committee records and other material on institutions, but this may not be 'local' to all the institutions of that authority - for example the London Metropolitan Asylums Board's Records can be found at Dartford in Kent! (See the chapter in this volume by Richard Harris.)

5. The fifth edition of Tredgold's work, published in 1929 has illustrations from the Royal Eastern Counties Institution. Some editions of the Medical Directory, which gives biographical details of doctors and locations of hospitals, lists Mental Deficiency Institutions in a separate section. Interwar periodicals, such as the *Journal of Mental Science, Mental Deficiency* and *Mental Welfare* regularly refer to events at individual institutions.

6. For more on this, see Chapters 1 and 3 in this volume.

7   Such as Maggie Potts and Rebecca Fido, '*A Fit Person to be Removed*', (Northcote House, 1991).

8. Examples include: Joanna Ryan and Frank Thomas, *The Politics of Mental Handicap*, (Free Association Books, 1987); P. Abbott and R. Sapsford, *Community Care for Mentally Handicapped Children*, (Milton Keynes, Open University Press, 1987). For a critique of these approaches, see Patricia Potts, 'What's the use of history? Understanding educational provisions for disabled students and those who experience difficulties in learning', *British Journal of Educational Studies*, 43, (1995), 398-411.

9. See articles by M. Brook and W. A. Heaton-Ward in S. Segal, *The Place of Special Villages and Residential Communities*, (AB Academic, Bicester, 1990); and Stephen Sands in R. Baron and J. D. Haldane, *Community Normality and Difference*, (Aberdeen University, 1992).

10. For an architectural analysis of nineteenth century asylums see A. Scull in A. King (ed.), *Buildings and Society: Essays on the Social Development of the Built Environment* (Routledge and Kegan Paul, 1980) pp.39-60; and in the United States, see W. Wolfensberger, *The Origin and Nature of our Institutional Models*, (New York, Human Policy Press, 1975).

11. H. C. Burdett, *Hospitals and Asylums of the World*, (Vol. 1, 1891), p.16.

12. Taken from the Annual Report, 1935.

Chapter 5

Images from the Past: Using Photographs

Mark Jackson

Summary

This chapter examines the use of a previously neglected set of sources, photographs, in exploring the history of learning disabilities. Focusing on photographs taken from the Sandlebridge Boarding Schools and Colony in the first few decades of this century, Mark Jackson argues that photographs can be used in conjunction with other historical sources to explain contemporary attitudes and policies concerning people with learning disabilities.

Introduction

In this chapter, I want to demonstrate how photographs can be used to increase our understanding of the histories of people with learning disabilities. The majority of the photographs that I shall discuss are taken from the early records of the Sandlebridge Boarding Schools and Colony in Great Warford in Cheshire.[1] I shall use the photographs from these records in three ways. Firstly, I shall explore how photographs can help us to understand the development and maintenance of a particular institution. Secondly, I shall discuss how photographs can help to explain how attitudes to people with learning disabilities determined the type of institutional care that was provided for them. In this context, I shall concentrate on photographs of work in the Sandlebridge Colony. Finally, I want to examine the ways in which photographs of residents in the Colony were used in medical textbooks and how they therefore contributed to contemporary attitudes towards people with learning disabilities.

The Sandlebridge Boarding Schools and Colony

At a meeting held in Manchester on 21st March 1899, members of the Lancashire and Cheshire Society for the Permanent Care of the Feeble-Minded agreed to establish an institution 'for the care, education, and welfare of feeble-minded persons'.[2] Local architects drew up plans for the buildings that satisfied guidelines set out in the 1899 Elementary Education (Defective and Epileptic Children) Act, namely that no such institution should comprise more than four houses each lodging no more than fifteen children.[3] The first two houses built on these lines, one for boys and one for girls, were opened in 1902.

Financial support from individual donations and subscriptions, from Local Education Authorities and Poor Law Unions throughout the country, and from the Department of Education allowed the Sandlebridge Boarding Schools to expand.[4] In the first three decades of this century, the Lancashire and Cheshire Society built, purchased or rented a number of buildings: new boarding houses for children and young adults; accommodation for the staff; a laundry, school room and hospital; farm buildings, land, and livestock; and a recreation hall.[5] This expansion allowed the Colony gradually to increase its residential capacity. In October 1909, there were 204 children in residence. By March 1919, the number had reached 283. Ten years later, in 1929, the total population of the Colony was 362. And in 1941, when the institution was transferred to Cheshire County Council, there were 422 children and adults resident in the Sandlebridge Colony.[6]

New building for 65 children (Erected 1905-6)

The Thomasson Day School circa 1905

This growth of Sandlebridge is well documented both in the Society's annual reports and in a series of illustrations in those reports charting the Schools' development. The annual reports include: plans for the first two houses built at Sandlebridge;[7] illustrations of the first houses shortly after they were opened;[8] details of the new buildings and land constructed, rented, or purchased;[9] and photographs of the dormitories and recreation rooms.[10] (See Figures 5.1 and 5.2) These illustrations enabled the Lancashire and Cheshire Society to advertise the nature and progress of the work that they were supporting.

Significantly, from a historical perspective, these photographs provide more than a simple story of Sandlebridge's expansion. They also reveal prominent attitudes to people referred to as 'feeble-minded' or 'mentally deficient' in this period. For example, fears that 'mental defectives' were a danger to society and should be prevented from having children found practical expression in the strict separation of the accommodation and school rooms for boys and girls, and young men and women, at Sandlebridge.[11]

The need to separate the school from other buildings also derived from beliefs about the nature and appropriate management of 'feeble-minded' children. According to Mary Dendy, one of the leading champions of permanent institutional care and honorary secretary to the Lancashire and Cheshire Society, it was 'most desirable that the school-house should be built quite apart from all the residential buildings of the colony. It is a great factor in the health of the children that they should be obliged to leave the house in which they live twice every day. It is not only that the fresh air lessens their liability to consumption, but also that it strengthens them in every way'.[12]

The inclusion of photographs of the buildings at Sandlebridge in the annual reports can be seen as part of the Lancashire and Cheshire Society's efforts to attract financial support for its institution. The extent to which writers of the Society's annual reports were sensitive to the interests of potential subscribers is evident in the photographs in the reports. In line with contemporary beliefs that so-called 'deviant' sections of the population should be trained to be orderly, decent and clean, it is noticeable that photographs of the rooms at Sandlebridge portrayed them as empty, tidy and clean rooms, devoid of human life.[13] (See Figure 5.3)

Photographs of institutions can therefore be used to illustrate the growth of an institution and to explore the ways in which that institution reflected and reinforced a variety of social, political, medical and educational beliefs about people with learning disabilities.

Dormitory in boys school circa 1903

Ploughing at Warford Hall Estate circa 1910

Photographic representations of work at Sandlebridge

From the start, occupation or work was a vital component of life at Sandlebridge. Occupation was seen to be important in two ways. Firstly, 'feeble-minded' children were thought to be happier when they were occupied. Secondly, certain forms of work contributed to the Colony's financial survival. By sewing, knitting, cleaning, laundering, farming and gardening, the young men and women at Sandlebridge contributed to their own maintenance. Of course, work also made administration easier. It was believed that children who were occupied would be less likely to succumb to what some writers referred to as 'bad habits, dirtiness and moral degradation.'[14] Similarly, physical labour was thought to be a 'good means of occupying and training those who are troublesome and robust.'[15]

The Lancashire and Cheshire Society's belief in productive work was reinforced in its annual reports by the inclusion of photographs of residents 'at work'. These photographs are of value to historians in at least two ways. Firstly, they allow us to reconstruct certain features of daily life in a colony at the turn of this century. Although the subjects of these photographs were probably carefully arranged to give the impression of order and discipline, the photographs nevertheless provide us with a visual record of the types of labour performed by residents and the manner in which that labour was divided between the young men and women.[16] (See Figure 5.4)

Photographs of workers also help us to explore contemporary beliefs in the social importance of work. Part of the Lancashire and Cheshire Society's initial success in attracting support for Sandlebridge rested on its ability to exploit fears about law and order, poverty, unemployment and crime, and about the general health and wealth of the population. According to the Lancashire and Cheshire Society's propaganda, work at Sandlebridge made 'mental defectives' self-sufficient. However, it also did much more than this. The reclamation of the land by 'feeble-minded' young men, clearly shown in photographs in the annual reports,[17] was thought to be the means by which 'deviants' themselves would be reclaimed and made useful.

Photographs of workers can therefore be used to enhance our understanding both of the day-to-day management of an institution and of the strategies adopted to legitimate that management.

Photographs of residents at Sandlebridge

Some of the photographs taken at Sandlebridge were included not only in the official records of the Lancashire and Cheshire Society for the Permanent Care of the Feeble-Minded but also in other publications. A photograph of the first buildings at Sandlebridge appeared in an article advertising the work of the Schools in *The Health Guardian* in 1903.[18] Photographs of some of the staff involved with the Schools also appeared in *The Health Guardian* and *Lancashire Faces and Places* during the first decade of this century.[19]

Photographs of residents at Sandlebridge were also included in a book on 'feeblemindedness'. One of the early casebooks of residents at Sandlebridge contains a collection of notes about the first 284 children admitted to the schools between 1902 and 1911.[20] The entries in this album include the name and date of birth of each child admitted, the source of maintenance fees, initial comments on the children's physical appearance, behaviour and educational ability, regular comments on their progress, and notes on their discharge or death.

These hand-written notes were supplemented by photographs of the children, most of which were taken between 1909 and 1911.[21] Significantly, some of these photographs were included in a medical text, *Feeblemindedness in Children of School-Age*, written for school medical officers, teachers and social workers by Charles Paget Lapage in 1911.[22] Lapage was a physician at the Manchester Children's Hospital at Pendlebury and a frequent visitor to Sandlebridge. Like other doctors writing on 'mental deficiency' (such as Alfred Tredgold, and George Shuttleworth and William Potts), Lapage made use of his institutional connections to gather illustrations for his medical text.[23]

Lapage used photographs of residents in two broad ways. Firstly, he used them to illustrate physical signs that could be used to diagnose certain congenital conditions thought to be associated with 'mental deficiency'.[24] Secondly, Lapage used photographs from Sandlebridge to demonstrate what was thought to be a strong link between physical appearance, on the one hand, and intellectual capacity and social ability, on the other. Photographs of children with supposedly 'defective expression' were used to support medical (and broader social) opinions that 'mental defectives' were also physically defective in some way.[25] According to Lapage, one only had 'to watch a group of feebleminded children to see that most of them have some peculiarity'.[26]

Through their inclusion in Lapage's book, photographs of residents at Sandlebridge served to reinforce a prominent belief that a certain section of the population was not only educationally 'substandard' but also physically abnormal or pathological.[27] Ironically, it was this belief that had led to the permanent segregation of residents at Sandlebridge in the first place. Careful analysis of photographs and of the ways in which they were used can therefore help us to understanding how segregation in institutions was used in the past and how it was supported by certain attitudes and beliefs.

Conclusion

In this chapter, I have tried to demonstrate the range of photographic material available in the records from one particular institution. In the process, I have attempted to suggest ways in which photographs can be interpreted and how those photographs can help us to develop a clearer picture of the history of people with learning disabilities. In particular, I have suggested that photographs can increase our understanding of the ways in which institutions have developed and of the strategies used to promote that development.

It is important to recognise that there may be legal and ethical restrictions on the use of photographic records. While photographs of an institution may be acceptable, photographs of individuals or groups of individuals should be used with caution. Under the Public Records Acts, access to institutional records can be restricted for many years unless permission is expressly granted, usually by the appropriate Health Authority. Many of the records at Sandlebridge, for example, are closed for a period of one hundred years from the date of the final entry. It is for this reason that, in this chapter, I have only used photographs of the institutions that were published in annual reports and therefore publicly available. Given that these publications often included photographs of residents, however, even these records should be reproduced with caution in order to safeguard the residents' rights to confidentiality.

Notes

1. Originally referred to as the Sandlebridge Boarding Schools and the Sandlebridge Colony, this institution became known as the Mary Dendy Homes in 1933 in memory of its founder, Mary Dendy, who died that year. In 1948, the Homes came under the control of the National Health Service, after which they became known as the Mary Dendy Hospital. In 1984, a phased run-down of the hospital was initiated in line with care-in-the-community policies. The hospital closed in 1989, when remaining residents were removed to the nearby Soss Moss Hospital.
    The Colony's records, in the Cheshire Record Office, Duke Street, Chester, include: NCh 1/6 (Annual Reports of the Lancashire and Cheshire Society for the Permanent Care of the Feeble-Minded); NHM 11/3837/42 (register of admissions to the Sandlebridge Special School); NHM 11/3837/43 (album of admissions to the Schools, with photographs); NHM 11/3837/47-49 (registers of residents, admissions and discharges, 1914-1970); NHM 11/3837/56- 58 (case books, 1914-1936); and NHM 11/3837/59-62 (medical officers' journals).

2. The Society's aims were outlined in the 'Constitution of the Lancashire and Cheshire Society for the Permanent Care of the Feeble-Minded', (1899).

3. Elementary Education (Defective and Epileptic Children) Act, 1899, 62 & 63 Vict. c.32.

4. This expansion was helped by amendments to the 1899 legislation, allowing such institutions to cater for increasing numbers of children: Elementary Education Amendment Act, 1903, 3 Edw. 7 c.13.

5. For detailed accounts of the funding, erection, and purchase of many of the new buildings, see the Annual Reports of the Lancashire and Cheshire Society for the Permanent Care of the Feeble-Minded (subsequently referred to simply as *Annual Reports*) for the years 1902, 1903, 1904, 1905, 1910-13, 1923, 1925-9.

6. These figures have been compiled from the *Annual Reports*, 1905-1929.

7. *Annual Report*, (1901), pp.2-3. The plans were drawn up by W. & G. Higginbottom, Architects, 94, Market Street, Manchester.

8. *Annual Report*, (1902), frontispiece; *Annual Report*, (1903), frontispiece.

9. *Annual Report*, (1905), between pp.8 and 9, and facing p.10; *Annual Report*, (1910), facing p. 10 and frontispiece.

10. *Annual Report*, (1904), between pp.8 and 9.

11. For contemporary discussions of the threat of mental deficiency, see, for example: Mary Dendy, *Feebleness of Mind, Pauperism and Crime*, (Glasgow, 1901); Mary Dendy, *The Problem of the Feeble-Minded*, (Manchester, 1908); and the papers by A. F. Tredgold ('The Problem of the Feeble-Minded') and Mary Dendy ('The Care of the Feeble-Minded'), presented at the Manchester and Salford Sanitary Association's Conference on the Care of the Feeble-minded in 1911 and published in the *Proceedings at a Conference on the Care of the Feebleminded*, (Manchester, 1911).

Introduction

Anyone who wishes to study the history of learning disability, or of particular learning disability institutions, in depth is likely to find themselves, sooner or later, in a local record office. Virtually all counties in England and Wales have one, and so do many metropolitan boroughs and London boroughs, and some other large towns.

All these offices receive records from many different sources. As well as Health Service institutions, these include private individuals, businesses, churches, charities, local authorities and courts. Almost all of these documents are held on loan. This means that what is received depends to a greater or lesser extent on the goodwill of the owners or custodians of the material. This is more or less true even in cases, like that of National Health Service Records, where there is legislation that attempts to secure the routine deposit of records.

The broad collecting policy adopted by all these offices means that they are very likely to hold a range of records relevant to the subject of learning disability, quite apart from those that derive directly from learning disability institutions. Documents from other sources may, for instance, throw light on the geographical setting of institutions, and how they fitted in to the local community, or may help to reconstruct the family relationships, and economic circumstances of individual patients, or the backgrounds and previous employment of staff.

Preserving institutional records

Although a few hospitals and health authorities have their own archivists, the historical records of most institutions, if they are available at all, will be in the county or other local authority record office. These are empowered to take such records (which are classed as Public Records), under the terms of the Public Records Acts 1958 and 1967. Hospitals and health authorities are governed in the matter of what records they should pass on to the record office by Department of Health circulars; the most recent one was issued in 1989[1]. In principle, these circulars envisage regular controlled transfers of selected records when they reach an age of 30 years. In practice, institutions usually only think about deposit when they are about to close, or when storage problems have reached crisis point. Often, the extent to which the need to preserve records is taken into consideration is dependent on the interest, or lack of it, of the staff on the spot. Archivists, most of whom have their own heavy workloads, cannot but sympathise with hard-pressed administrators. On most scales of values, there are more important things to do than secure the safe keeping of obsolete records. Often, the task of deciding what is to be kept, and what destroyed, is left to archivists from the record office who are called in at short notice and given *carte blanche* to make decisions.

The practical effect of this is that researchers are far more likely to be able to find records of institutions that have closed, than of those that are still open. In the case of these closed institutions, a disproportionate amount of material is likely to date from their last few years of operation.

To take an actual example, South Ockendon Hospital, a learning disability institution in south west Essex, which closed in 1994. At its peak, in the 1960s, the 'colony', as it was originally known, housed over 1000 residents. It occupied an 84-acre site, with a chapel, sick bay, school, workshops and residential 'villas'. There was also a 98-acre hospital farm[2].

The County Archivist of Essex was first alerted to the imminent closure of the hospital in February 1994, and had until the end of May to organise and carry out the selection and removal of those records that were wanted. Altogether, record office staff spent fifteen person-days on site carrying out the selection.

Archivists worked while demolition work went on around them, sorting out the large and valuable archive covering the hospital's whole history from its foundation in 1932 to its closure. In this time, it had been both

South Ockendon Hospital

Commemorative Stone

celebrated as a pioneer of advanced and civilised standards of care and had subsequently become notorious for appalling scandals[3]. The archive will be an outstanding source for future generations of medical and social historians. It is not, however, complete; no archive ever really is. For a start, the records of the hospital's beginnings will at least partly be found among those of the former County Borough of West Ham, which founded it. These are held by the present London Borough of Newham.

All records of on-going administrative value were transferred to successor institutions, including all the individual patients' files. Nevertheless, the record office had a great deal of material to select from. Preservation went beyond what is laid down in the Department of Health circulars, and the archivists retained far more material relating to day to day clinical care than these specify, even though it will all have to be closed, for most purposes, for 100 years. Standard archival theories about how to select were of limited help. Received wisdom is that 'policy' files are what, above all, should be retained. In fact such a neat division between policy and non-policy files rarely exists. Guidelines on selection always start from the premise that the entire body of records is available to start with; this is rarely actually true, certainly not in the case of South Ockendon.

In a number of areas, records were specifically chosen for the information they gave about named individuals, residents or staff. Family historians or amateur genealogists are a county record office's largest single group of users, and their needs have to be borne in mind. It was also necessary to take into account other factors, such as the light that records might throw on the wider history of the community in which the institution was situated.

At South Ockendon, despite the presence of bulldozers, the Essex Record Office became involved just soon enough. If the warning of the closure of an institution reaches the local record office too late, records may be received from it in total disorder or, at worst, be lost completely. Predicting the arrival of new collections of archives is rarely easy. One week may bring a handful of documents, the next a lorry-load. Often it is some crisis or major upheaval which causes people to clear out their archives and pass them to their local record office or their dustman. The bankruptcy of a business, a change of premises by a solicitor, the death of a local antiquary, the closure of an institution - all involve archivists in a hurried operation to rescue archives which are threatened with homelessness and often destruction. Occasionally news only filters through to the record office when archives have actually reached the skip.

Using local archives

In the case of South Ockenden, many documents were saved and are now on deposit in the Essex Record Office. They are being preserved for historians and researchers to refer to in studying the history of learning disability. We turn now to the question of how people who are interested in history can find and use such valuable records in their own local record office.

The way in which archives are stored and made available in local record offices is quite different from that found in a library. The sheer quantity, the uniqueness, value and (sometimes) the fragility, of archival material, means that it cannot be on open access. It has to be stored in secure and air conditioned strongrooms, and brought to the searchroom for users on request. For these reasons, detailed catalogues have to be compiled, so that users can identify what they require. Records are grouped according to their origin, not according to subject. The records from South Ockendon Hospital will, for instance, form a single group. Each group is given a separate catalogue, and each document given its own unique reference number for identification. The user will be asked to quote these reference numbers when requesting documents.

In order to protect the originals, increasing use is made of microfilm or microfiche copies; but it is still necessary to consult the catalogues and use the reference numbers. It is not usually advisable to go straight to the catalogue to find references to particular names or subjects. The normal procedure is to consult the office's indexes. These have the same relation to the body of catalogues as the index to a book has to its contents. Most county record offices will have three basic indexes, to people, places and subjects.

Many record offices are beginning to make considerable investment in computerisation. There is much misunderstanding about this. They are not by and large transferring the data in the archives they hold into machine-readable form. This would be inconceivably expensive. Neither are they, at present, storing images of records to any great extent, although this will be done increasingly over the coming years to protect the original documents, as film and fiche are used at present. What many offices, Essex among them, are beginning to do is to hold catalogues and indexes on computer. This will not change the basic procedure of research, but it will make the task easier and quicker; and the catalogues, and in particular the indexes, will be far more comprehensive than they are now.

Users should find local record offices welcoming and easy to use. In most cases the service is free. Most require users to take out a reader's ticket, but this is for security and identification reasons. No proof of academic *bona fides* or serious intent is normally required; local offices pride themselves on being open to all. It is advisable to book a place in advance, as searchrooms can get very busy. The phone number will be found under the appropriate county or other council.

If the researcher is looking for the records of a particular institution, it is essential to check first that the record office actually has them. They may not have been deposited, or local authority boundary changes may mean that they are not in the office that seems the logical one, but somewhere else. There may be particular problems in making available large quantities of records at a time. Different offices have different rules about making available records that are not yet catalogued. It is useful if the researcher can tell the record office in advance as much about their line of research as possible. They should not, however, rely entirely on the archivist to select relevant items. It is always advisable to read the catalogues thoroughly. Although archivists and other searchroom staff try to be as helpful as possible, the user must remember that their time is limited, and they have to ration the amount that they can devote to any one individual.

If the researcher comes to a record office knowing what to expect, he or she should find using its resources a rewarding and pleasurable experience.

Conclusion

The local record office has to be a port of call for anyone seriously interested in local history. It is almost certainly rich in local resources which are there, preserved, for interested people to delve into and explore. But those riches cannot be taken for granted - often they are there only because they have been rescued from loss or destruction through the swift action of archivists. The record office's role is thus twofold: to rescue and preserve local documents, and to make them available and accessible to those who wish to use them.

Notes

1. Department of Health (1989) *Health Circular HC* (89)20. London, Dept. of Health.

2. A fuller account of South Ockendon hospital is available. This is in the form of an official history, commissioned in the last stages of the hospital's life:

    Bingley, R. (1995) *South Ockendon: Echoes from an Essex Hospital*. South Ockendon Hospital publication.

3. South Ockendon Hospital was the subject of an official enquiry in the early 1970s:

    Report of the Committee of Inquiry into South Ockendon Hospital, HMSO, 1974.

Chapter 7

Telling the History of Learning Disability from Local Sources

Jan Walmsley

Summary

In this chapter, Jan Walmsley explores how a local history of learning disability can be built up from a range of sources. Using Bedfordshire as an example, she shows how an historical account of learning disability can be woven together using oral history, archives, books, pamphlets and newspapers as primary sources. This approach to local history can be used by readers wherever they happen to live or work.

Introduction

In recent years there has been a resurgent interest on the part of historians in mental handicap hospitals, largely because they are scheduled for closure. Those large institutions in remote countryside, which housed large numbers of people with learning disabilities, are the focus of the chapters by Fido and Potts, and by Andy Stevens, in this book. But we still have precious little knowledge of community care and the smaller institutions which sustained those people who lived outside hospital, who were always the majority. This chapter sets out to explain how local historians might get involved in documenting this particular aspect of local history as part of a larger enterprise of reclaiming a lost history. It should be read in conjunction with Chapter 8 which expands on one particular approach, the use of archive sources.

A range of sources

The local historian who wishes to study some aspect of the history of learning disability in the twentieth century has a range of sources to draw on. As I have been involved in historical research in Bedfordshire I use primarily that county's sources for illustration.

Archives

By archives I mean here those documents which are preserved for the use of historians, and others. The immediate source for most people in setting out to find out about local history is their county record office (see Chapter 6 by Richard Harris). County record offices often hold records of the Mental Deficiency Committees which were set up to administer the 1913 Mental Deficiency Act on behalf of local authorities. Bedfordshire, for example, has a remarkably intact set of records relating to its Committee. As well as formal minutes, the records include most of the Clerk's correspondence with Poor Law Boards of Guardians, families, institutions, voluntary organisations (such as the National Association for Mental Welfare) and the Board of Control, the national regulatory body for the Act.

Soon after 1946, when the NHS came into being, these Mental Deficiency Committees were replaced by sub-committees of the County Council, usually called Mental Health or Mental Treatment sub-committees because they dealt with both mental illness and learning disability. In Bedfordshire, these post-war sources are less informative than their pre-1946 counterparts, largely because many of the day to day activities were in the hands of employees of the mental health services rather than the Clerk, and have not therefore found their way into the record office. However, formal minutes continue to give insight into the major

Two sketches of Bromham Hospital

developments such as the setting up of occupation centres; the numbers of people in hospital, discharged or under supervision in their homes; the appointment of staff; and the administration of Guardianship orders. The local historian will almost certainly find in them at least a framework of major service developments.

Some record offices, for example, Greater London, have individual patient records covering long periods in people's lives. As these relate to individuals they are subject to closure for eighty or a hundred years after the date of the final entry, and there are real ethical problems in using such sources for publication. However, in due course they will provide rich insights into the lives of people who rarely leave much in the way of written memoirs.

There are more sources for this history in county record offices, catalogued, for example, under Education, or relating to Boards set up to administer 'colonies', the predecessors of mental handicap hospitals. In Bedfordshire there are files relating to the Joint Board set up to administer Bromham House Colony (as Bromham Hospital was known) with Northamptonshire and Northampton County Borough which sat from 1931 to 1946. Some areas like Essex also have records relating to institutions set up by charitable bodies prior to the 1913 Act which encouraged all local authorities to found a colony.

What kind of things are found in these archived documents? Inter alia, they provide insights into attitudes of officialdom to people with learning disabilities, ranging from censure to pity, and these attitudes appear to change over time. For example, in 1915 Florence B was reported to the Mental Deficiency Committee after she was:

> spoken to by a soldier who persuaded her to go for a walk with him. The subsequent movements are not known, but Mrs B states that her daughter's clothing was disarranged.

According to the report to the Committee by the Deputy County Medical Officer of Health, Florence, then aged 14, was 'dull and lethargic, of a muddy appearance and tremulous about the lips'. She was able to read, but, said the report, 'does not understand what she has read'. She was certified as a moral imbecile, and sent to a certified home in Alton, Hampshire[1]. Such documents testify to the loss of civil liberties for people so labelled, and who were often confined to institutions for a lifetime.

Later, the reports are more benign in tone, and frequently the actions of the certifying officers are presented as being in the best interests of the person. One of the quarterly reports filed by Miss Mumford, Bedfordshire's voluntary visitor to 'mental defectives' who remained in their parental homes, remains for 1935. Of Geoffrey G, aged 8, Miss Mumford writes:

> This little lad looks very frail although I understand he is being allowed cod liver oil and malt. The father is unemployed due to illness, and the family are on relief. The home is a poor one, but I think the parents do their best for the lad. Geoffrey is a nice little

lad and one whom I think would benefit by training. I have not at present suggested it to the parents. Would the Committee wish that I should do so?[2]

'Training' meant a hospital place, probably for many years.

These are anecdotes. A lot more analysis of this type of material is needed to build a clear picture of policy and practice. Bedfordshire, for example, was a local authority which provided few institutional places before World War 2, and it would be interesting to make comparisons with what were, in contemporary eyes, more progressive authorities which actively sought out 'defectives' - such as Somerset, Birmingham or London. It is an ideal field for local historians to make an impact. (More ideas about the use of archives are to be found in Chapters 8 and 9).

Of course, the thirty year rule which prohibits public access to many official papers until thirty years after publication will preclude investigation of the most recent history through archives. In order to uncover this recent history, as well as gain an 'unofficial' insight into earlier periods, the local historian will need to look elsewhere.

Local Printed Sources
The availability of local printed sources will inevitably vary from place to place, so this section can only indicate some possibilities. There can be few hospitals, for example, which have not attracted the attention of someone at some time. Such accounts may be found in the reference section of major public libraries, or may be housed in county record offices which usually have a comprehensive selection of local publications on their shelves. Relevant to Bedfordshire I found *A History of the Three Counties Asylum* at Fairfield[3] which at times in its history housed some men with learning disabilities, as well as the 'lunatics' which it primarily served. I also came across the *History of Leavesden Hospital, Hertfordshire*[4], where a number of Bedfordshire residents found themselves when Bromham House, their local 'colony, was full or deemed inappropriate because it did not cater for people who were likely to abscond, or were severely disabled. Such histories are usually celebratory, and concentrate on uncontroversial aspects of the hospital's development, like new buildings or staff changes, but rarely discussing the minutiae of individual lives.

Some local histories, for example of education, will cover special schools to a limited extent. Thus Dony's *History of Education in Luton*[5] has a few pages on special education. Some local firms, like Rowntree Mackintosh in Norwich, had a policy of employing people with learning disabilities, and they may have produced their own histories. Regrettably, Bedfordshire's general histories do not embrace learning disability. This may not always be the case, so it is worth looking.

Often prominent members of local authorities will undertake a descriptive account of their own service. I was fortunate enough to find in the excellent Bedford Local History Library a *History of the Development of the Mental Health Services in Bedfordshire 1946 to 1970* written by an ex-Poor Law Relieving Officer who had become a Mental Health Officer and later rose to be Deputy Director of Social Services. It was invaluable for dates, statistics and photographs, as well as providing an insight into attitudes at the time of writing.[6] The author became one of my oral history interviewees in my research, so it was a doubly rich source. Another example of an informative account, this time on the health side, is by Dr Morris, Medical Superintendent of Little Plumstead Hospital in Norfolk, which described the way the Hospital provided out-reach services (1959).

A local historian might come across some local investigations under-taken to give insight into a perceived social problem at the time. An example in my own area is Tomlinson's *Enquiry into Problem Families in Luton*,[7] one of five local studies sponsored by the Eugenics Society in the 1940s. Tomlinson was inclined to link problem families with mentally defective parents, as one might expect from a report sponsored by the Eugenics Society. As 'mental deficiency' was then seen to be correlated with 'problem families' it is a useful source for uncovering attitudes as well as documenting social conditions, ideas about solutions, and existing services.

Local voluntary organisations also produce printed material. I found the Year Books of Luton Mencap from 1959 onwards in the possession of one of its founder members (there were only one or two editions in the local libraries) and made extensive use of them. They give quite a different perspective from that produced from examining the records left by statutory bodies. As well as news about membership, fund raising and the work of the committee, they include photographs, articles written by local service providers describing the facilities they offer, and letters from parents. Luton's Year Books include detailed descriptions of the opening of major facilities, such as the adult training centre in 1966, and the adult hostel in 1972. Both of these facilities are still in existence, and it is instructive to compare the optimism attendant upon their opening with the criticisms levelled at such 'mini-institutions' today.

There may also be copies of leaflets explaining what services are available, programmes marking the opening of new facilities, like schools, and reports commissioned by social services departments. These are likely to be found in local libraries and cover most recent events, from the sixties onwards.

Local newspapers are an obvious source of information, particularly on attitudes to 'mental handicap', and on the debates around service development. I found features in the following categories after a search through three local papers from 1958 to 1990:

- reports on charitable events - the Vauxhall Apprentices' pram race, which took place in Luton annually and whose proceeds went to Luton Mencap, is faithfully recorded annually for 10 years in the 1960s and 1970s

- human interest stories, such as 'brave parents battle against the odds for their unfortunate child' and 'unfortunate parents desperately need hospital place'

- campaigning/information giving about the condition: often these try to promote a more positive image of people with mental handicaps, as innocent child-like people, to combat fears stimulated by proposals to open community-based facilities.

Oral History

Oral history interviews offer two advantages over the written sources. Firstly, they are not subject to restriction or closure, so they can give information about very recent periods. Secondly, they offer the chance to get the inside story from people who were subject to the policies and practices you read about in the written sources. The veracity and authenticity of oral history have been much debated, and I do not intend to dwell upon those aspects here. Paul Thompson's book *The Voice of the Past*[8] discusses these issues much better than I can.

The first decision that needs to be made is who to interview. It will, of course, depend upon the topic chosen, and whose voices are to be featured. I chose to try to include in my research a range of people: parents, members of voluntary bodies, staff and people with learning disabilities, so that I could demonstrate that the same events looked very different, depending upon who you were.

Locating informants is perhaps the most difficult task. Most texts on oral history recommend finding people who are articulate and have a good story to tell, but of course there is no way of ensuring that in advance, unless the interviewer knows them already. Few people with learning difficulties fall into the 'articulate' category anyway, although Mabel Cooper's life story in this book shows what can be achieved. I found most of my informants through a key figure in the local Mencap Society, a founder member, now in her seventies, whose son was born in the 1940s. She knows (almost) everyone, and once I had explained my purpose, she put her network at my disposal as best she could. She herself was a key interviewee. She remembers all the key events from the early 1950s, and could provide me with two important dimensions, a personal experience of having a severely disabled child at a time when facilities were almost non-existent, and a quasi-professional view as long time Chair of Luton Mencap.

Some memories are very moving. She recalled putting her son, Colin, into Bromham House hospital in 1958:

> It is a very hard decision. I should think for 18 months after the decision I cried myself to sleep. I felt like a murderess. I really felt I had condemned him to death. And that was really when I threw myself into Mencap, heart and soul. I thought you know I must fight for all those who are in the community because perhaps those parents won't have to undergo this trauma.[9]

Because my main aim was to hear the life stories of people with learning difficulties, they formed the bulk of my interviewees, interviewed individually, or in pairs. My focus was not specifically history so much as individual biographies. Nevertheless, some interviews provided corroboration of information I had gleaned from documentary sources, whilst at the same time maintaining a distinctive personal perspective. Of her time in hospital, Isobel recalled:

> I got locked in. I had lovely hair right down my back. And they cut it. They tie me in a chair. I refuse. Tied me in a chair cos I didn't want my hair cut. They cut it all short by scissors. 'Cos they didn't want long hairs in hospital. It was like that. Then after that got punished. They put me in a dark room on a mattress. Quarter/half hour, then they took me out and injected me. Yeah. Long while ago.[10]

Although this is very much in line with oral testimonies from another hospital documented in Potts and Fido's book *'A Fit Person to be Removed'* (1991)[11] it is in stark contrast to 'official' accounts. The Board of Control Inspectors' reports in the late thirties and forties, for example, consistently praise Bromham. And in 1966, roughly at the time Isobel was there, the Medical Superintendent wrote:

> We care for the mentally subnormal. At Bromham we prepare patients to return to the community. It is the place where the actors learn their lines.[12]

My parent informant herself, despite her guilt at putting Colin away, said 'It (Bromham) was quite marvellous in those days'. I doubt if Isobel would have recognised the place she lived in from these descriptions! The importance of a range of views cannot be overstated when dealing with a topic such as this.

An alternative approach to oral history with people with learning disabilities is to assemble a 'reminiscence' group, so that people can spark off one another's memories. This will require co-operation from homes, hostels, adult literacy class or adult training centres, largely because of transport problems, but the experience of my colleague, Dorothy Atkinson, suggests this may well be worthwhile.[13] Alternatively, adult education classes may be a way of locating a group willing to talk about the past.

It is important to have a focus for the work. There are a large range of possibilities, for example:

- the work of the voluntary sector, Mencap especially, (ENABLE in Scotland), as it has a lot of older members, is the longest established parents' body and celebrated its 50th anniversary in 1996;

- individual units such as hospitals, or hospital wards, occupation centres (now called adult training centres, social education centres or resource centres), hostels, sheltered workshops, or children's homes;

- the memories of hospital staff and residents;

- individual biographies of patients, parents or staff;

- the roles of seaside landladies or foster homes;

- religious foundations which specialised in caring for 'mental defectives';

- the work of local authority employees.

Making sense and writing up

It is one thing locating sources, and quite another to thread together a coherent story. This is exacerbated by the relative absence of already published histories, national or local. This means the local historian has both to construct a large scale map, and fill in the local detail. Clearly, there is a place for a basic framework of key dates, and personalities, as a contribution to the large scale mapping. Such a map is urgently needed if there is ever to be a broad view of what happened where and when. But what of the individual stories, the anecdotes, the differing perspectives? How are these best represented? One way to approach it seems to be to accept that the same events, ideas, and policies look very different depending upon whose perspective is adopted. I found this description of George C. in the archives of 1935:

> When I visited this case I saw Mr C. (father) about the lad being sent away for training ... as there is no mother and the lad is left all day without supervision I feel it would be the best thing that could happen to him. This lad is quite trainable[14].

George turned up in the 1990s as a member of Dorothy Atkinson's reminiscence group. This is his memory of the events following the recommendation that he be sent for 'training':

> I was in Bromham 20 years. I went there in 1938, March 3rd. I ain't got any photos. I had ever so many at home before I went to Bromham, but you know I didn't have time because the people came to fetch me so bloomin' early in the morning[15].

Conclusion

Maybe it is best to leave these two contrasting accounts to speak for themselves. There are many voices to be heard. The local historian can give them a platform.

Notes

1. This is pieced together from papers filed in Mental Deficiency Papers (MDP) Vol.1 in the Beds County Record Office (CRO)

2. Filed in Beds CRO MDP Vol.23

3. A. S. Monk, *A History of the Three Counties Asylum, Fairfield Hospital.* (Stotfold, Hitchin, 1960)

4. Monica Diplock, *The History of Leavesden Hospital* (private publication, 1990)

5. A. Dony, *History of Education in Luton* (Luton, Luton Museums Service, 1970)

6. Cecil French, *A History of the Development of the Mental Health Services* (Bedfordshire County Council, 1972)

7. G. Tomlinson, *Families in Trouble; an enquiry into Problem Families in Luton* (Luton, Gibbs Bamforth and Co., 1946)

8. Paul Thompson, *The Voice of the Past* Second edition (Oxford University Press, 1989)

9. Taken from the transcription of an interview conducted as part of my research in 1992.

10. Extract from one of my research interviews, 1992.

11. Maggie Potts and Rebecca Fido, *A Fit Person to be Removed* (Plymouth, Northcote House, 1991) The Chapter by Fido and Potts in this book describes the project

12. Quoted in the Luton Society of Mentally Handicapped Children Year Book, 1966

13. Dorothy Atkinson's edited reminiscences of a group of Bedfordshire adults with learning difficulties, *Past Times* has been privately published and is available free from the author

14. Beds CRO, MDP1

15. Quoted in Atkinson's *Past Times*, p.41.

Chapter 8

Uncovering Community Care: Evidence in a County Record Office

Jan Walmsley

Summary

In this chapter, Jan Walmsley focuses on using archive sources to uncover the history of community care. This includes looking at what local records are available, and how they can be accessed and used to shed light on the past. The records used and cited here are from the Bedfordshire County Record Office's set of papers from the Mental Deficiency Committee, 1915-1946. Similar records are kept in other local record offices. The challenge is for those records to be used to build local accounts of the history of community care.

Introduction

This chapter examines the potential of documents archived in county record offices for uncovering the history of community care before World War II. The documents cited here all come from the Bedfordshire County Record Office's holdings of the papers for the county's Mental Deficiency Committee 1915-1946. County record offices will vary in the amount of information they hold on this subject and Bedfordshire's records are exceptionally rich.

The Bedfordshire Mental Deficiency Committee was set up to administer the 1913 Mental Deficiency Act in the county. The Act made local authorities responsible for (i) the ascertainment of all persons 'subject to be dealt with' (ii) the provision and maintenance of suitable institutions (iii) the care of mental defectives in the community, including the conveyance of patients to and from institutions and the care of cases under guardianship orders; and (iv) the supervision of cases where neither institutional care nor statutory guardianship appeared necessary. Briefly, Bedfordshire's Mental Deficiency Committee met for the first time in 1915 and set up a scheme, approved by the Board of Control, for implementation of the Act.

Bedfordshire was relatively slow to implement the Act. In 1926 there were only 17 'defectives' under supervision at home and 67 in institutions. In Somerset, which is the subject of the next chapter, by Dorothy Atkinson, the corresponding figures were 1,131 and 399 in the same year.[1]

An indication of the county's implementation of the Act can be found in the Board of Control's 'league tables', published annually. In Board of Control terms 'good' local authorities had high levels of ascertainment (identification) of mental defectives; 'bad' local authorities had low rates. Bedfordshire was, in 1937, fifth from bottom of this league. This was partly because it did not have its own colony until 1931, and this colony was very small until the late 1930s. Until then, all institutionalised defectives were either sent out of county or housed in Poor Law Institutions.

After 1931 the papers of the Joint Board responsible for Bromham House (the local colony) provide an additional resource for the study of learning disability in Bedfordshire. However I have not included these here because the focus is on 'community care' rather than on the history of institutions.

Bedfordshire County Records: Mental Deficiency Committee

MDC General Correspondence 1914-1948

This series contains the clerk's correspondence, both incoming and out-going. They are filed in date order.

They include documents and circulars of national interest, for example from the Board of Control and the National Association for Mental Welfare, as well as local correspondence and circular letters from institutions advertising vacancies with costs. A lot of the correspondence relates to requests for leave of absence from institutions and payment by families of their contribution to the costs of keeping 'defectives' in institutions.

MDM Minutes 1914-1947

These are typed minutes of the Committee which met quarterly. They are a summary of the previous quarter's activities and include decisions on individual cases as well as broader policy. Overall they are fairly repetitive and take up themes which are found in more detail in the Clerk's correspondence.

MDL Letter Books 1914-1941

These books contain all the clerk's letters.

MDP Papers 1915-1947

These files contain the papers relating to the quarterly meetings. They include hand-written minutes, reports from the Deputy Medical Officer of Health's visits and decisions over certification, with reasons; correspondence from institutions where Bedfordshire 'defectives' were living, including quarterly reports on residents; requests for discharge from the Act's provision; letters about orders for detention for one or five years; Board of Control letters to the committee; reports from the Voluntary Visitor who visited defectives in their homes quarterly; licences to Poor Law Institutions to house defectives; letters from parents; annual reports from institutions where Bedfordshire residents were placed.

Overall the MDP series were the most informative both on policy and on individual cases. The examples which follow illustrate the range of topics on which this series of papers sheds light. The class marks - MDP 23, for example, - refer to the files or boxes in which these papers are stored, and are the reference numbers which a researcher will need to use when requesting documents in a county record office.

In the examples which follow, all surnames have been abbreviated to initials, although in the original papers full names and addresses are used. As this is potentially a sensitive area for families it seems best to anonymise information as far as possible.

Example 1: Individual Case

MDP1 *Report from the Deputy County Medical Officer of Health on Dora Ann S., aged 21, 29/6/1915*

Dora S. was referred by the Luton Rescue Home for Girls in Luton. She had been found wandering and without visible means of support. The DCMOH filled in some background:

> 'At the Court it was alleged that the girl was a menace to the troops as she had been sleeping with various soldiers in the neighbourhood and complaints had been made by the military to the police of the girl's conduct' ...

His medical report includes the following:

> 'her appearance is healthy, but somewhat dull and .... I am of the opinion that she has not got sufficient mental control to resist men who wish to assault her, but on the contrary her mental condition is such that she accepts these attentions from men, failing to appreciate the immorality of her conduct'

She could do housework and answer questions but, he wrote:

> 'when questioned she becomes nervous... is continually chattering and when alone talks aloud'.

Reports were sought from Dora's mother. The DCMOH summarised what she said: *'had always been dull at school ... after school she entered domestic service. Three years ago her mother was sent for by the girl's mistress as she was behaving immorally with the farm hands.' Until her daughter was assaulted whilst in this situation she exhibited no immoral tendencies, but from that time until the present she appears to have been immoral whenever opportunity has occurred. Mr T. (stepfather) states that neither he nor his wife will receive the girl into their house as during the time she was living there she accused Mr T. of attempting immoral conduct with her.*
In all probability Dora S is not pregnant at the present time. Moral Imbecile'

In the minutes of the 12th October 1915 meeting it was recorded that Dora was sent to Clifton House, Uxbridge Road, London which specialised in 'fallen girls'.

Commentary

This case highlights some salient features of the operation of the 1913 Mental Deficiency Act. Girls were targeted for immoral behaviour, particularly sexual misconduct, and the blame was attached to Dora, rather than the men who approached her. She was also blamed for accusing Mr T. of attempting immoral conduct. Her appearance is of significance because it was believed that deficiency could be detected by visible 'stigmata'. Her competence in performing tasks such as housework or answering questions is acknowledged, but undermined by the comment on her 'chattering' and 'talking aloud'. As it was a pre-condition of certification under the Act that the defect had been present from an early age it was important that Dora's mother's evidence testified to this.

Example 2:

MDP23 Model Form issued by the Board of Control, January 1929, for completion by the Deputy County Medical Officer of Health or Voluntary Visitor on visiting a defective's home
(This is an example of a completed form. The visit was occasioned by a request for financial assistance from the defective's mother.)

Form for the Information of the Visitors when carrying out their statutory duties under Section 11 of the Mental Deficiency Act, 1913 in regard to the defective named.

Name *E. D. I.*

Date of Birth *12/2/23*

Certified form of defect *Feeble minded - mongol type*

How Subject to be dealt with:

1 **Condition of home to which the patient would be:**
  (i) Licensed:

  GUARDIANSHIP - FAIR

  (ii) Discharged:

(a) **Composition of household:**

  Grandfather aged 77 years. Mother aged 56 years. Brother aged 20 years, sister aged 18 years and patient.

(b) **Condition of House:**

  (Number of rooms, cleanliness, locality, etc) Four rooms. Council House. Fairly clean. Locality good.

(c) Sleeping Accommodation:
>> *Three bedrooms.*

(d) Financial position of family:
>> *Mrs I. receives widow's pension 10/-.*
>> *Grandfather pays 10/- for Board. Son*
>> *pays 15/- and daughter 12/- for Board.*
>> *Total £2.7.0d. per week.*

(e) Facilities for the supervision and care of the patient:
>> *Fairly good.*

(f) Is it considered that the control available would suffice to prevent the defective from procreating children?
>> *Patient always in the care of either*
>> *grandfather or mother.*

2 Prospects of employment or occupation at house:
>> *None*

Children in bed at time of visit 9.15 am. Is able to wash and dress herself Quite clean in person. Mother would like to keep child under her own care, if possible, but finds the financial position rather strained.

Signed   *E. A. T............*

Date   *28th April 1937*

(Model form enclosed with circular letter from Board of Control No.717, dated January 1929).

Commentary

This form shows us what detailed surveillance families were subject to if they had a 'defective' son or daughter. It is particularly interesting that the visitor commented on the cleanliness of the home, as this suggests families were subject to moral judgements. Question (f) about procreating children shows just how concerned the authorities were to regulate sexual conduct and reproduction.

Example 3:

MDP 23 Quarterly Report of the Bedfordshire Voluntary Association for the Care of the Mentally Defective, 30/4/1937

This is an extract from the Report of Miss M., the Voluntary Visitor, who visited 'defectives' in their homes every quarter, and reported on each individual to the Committee. Miss M. was a member of the Beds Voluntary Association for the Care of the Mentally Defective. The use of lady volunteers for visiting was standard practice in the inter-war years. Miss M. had 56 people on her books at this time.

Quarterly Report of the Bedfordshire Voluntary Association for the Care of the Mentally Defective.

Alice M. - Aged 17 - Maulden:

Alice is well cared for and the home is a good one. The girl helps her mother in the house and with younger members of the family. Alice is in good health.

Olive S. - Aged 26 - Streatley:

In spite of the girl's paralysis it is wonderful the amount of tasks she can perform in the house and she helps her grandmother all she can.

Kate C. - Aged 48 - Cardington:

Kate is in good health and is well cared for in an excellent home and she looks much better than when her mother was alive. The son-in-law with whom she lives has insisted upon her taking a share in the household duties and the improvement in her is most marked and she looks happy and well cared for.

Edwin S. - Aged 33 - Ampthill

This man who took his discharge from the Ampthill Institution in October last is now living at 3, Council Houses, Colmworth. The master gave me this information having obtained it through some one in the Institution to whom S. had written. It would appear that he is working on a farm. Is it the wish of the Committee that I should visit S. in his lodgings there?.

Beatrice S. - Aged 18 - Marston Moreteyne

Looking better, clean and smart. The home is a poor one, although there does not appear to be a lack of money.

Commentary

This document shows in detail the degree of surveillance families were subject to. It is particularly interesting that the Visitor praised girls for being of help in the house, thus reinforcing gender roles. And some families were clearly in Miss M's good books for being caring and clean, presumably because they reflected her views of a 'good' family.

Example 4: Letters from families

These are fairly common in the MDP and MDC files, usually to do with maintenance payments or leave requests.

(a) Letter from F.M.O. dated 22/4/1937 requesting leave for his sister, Florence (MDP23).

I am the only one who goes (sic) to see her. I thought a change would do her good to being in there. She had never had a holiday since her father died.

(b) Letter from parents re maintenance payments dated 4/11/1940 (MDP26).

My son has been away now from here since 1917: a lifetime really and there seems no hope of his ever coming home. It is nearly two years since we saw him as I know the railway fare is too high and the train service is so bad. I should love to see my only son, but I know it's awkward. I tried to send him a packet of cigarettes every week. It is trouble enough him being away, especially such a distance ...

(c) Letters from 'defectives'

These are extremely rare. Here is one, dated 26/1/1943 from Ruth G. (MDP27):

Dear Madame or Sir,

I wonder if you would in any way do me a great favour. All I want is to ask you if could you by any means help me to get discharge of the care and control. As this is my 21 years I have done under your care and control. I am 26 years old. I done 15 years and 6 months at Stoke Park and 12 months as Bromham House. But I am at Springfield House in service for 4 years and 4 months. This is the first time I have wrote to you. Nothing like sticking up for yourself... But I must thank you for putting me under your care in the first place. I don't know where I would have been, but now I am able to look after myself!

(She was discharged after consultation with the Medical Superintendent of the institution who made favourable reference to her 'good moral character', and the fact that her sister and mother lived locally.)

Commentary

Letters from families, and 'defectives', represent one of the few ways (along with oral history) in which the researcher can gain access to the 'voices' of people other than law makers, doctors and administrators.

What can you find out from local records?

Statistics: regular reports on numbers of people certified, where they live, males, females, category (moral imbecile/idiot etc) make it possible to chart fluctuations in the implementation of the Act. Statistics are also included on the numbers of people on licence, under guardianship, under supervision at home, in institutions and state institutions.

Interaction between national and local policy: it is possible to trace the local response to national policy initiatives. This is made relatively simple because national circulars are filed on the date received, and repercussions, if any, can be found in the Committee minutes.

Details of how policy translated into practice: including process of certification (Example 1): applications for leave (Examples 2 and 4a) role of voluntary organisations (Example 3); discharge (Example 4c); applications for licence and guardianship; assessments for maintenance payments and arrears chasing.

Attitudes: to gender, class and mental deficiency on the part of the local authority and its officials (Examples 1 and 3).

Costs and Expenditure: how much was spent on institutional places, medical care and subsistence grants to families.

Individual biographies: movements can be traced over the years, especially people who moved frequently, caused trouble, or were under Guardianship (Example 1).

Information on Institutions: in addition to details of Bromham House, the local colony, annual reports are filed on the institutions where Bedfordshire defectives were placed. Quarterly reports from institutions to the Mental Deficiency Committee on the progress of Bedfordshire residents are also a source for institutional histories. The Bromham House Annual Reports, in conjunction with papers of the Joint Board for Bromham, are particularly informative.

What can't you find out?

The viewpoints of parents and 'defectives': the records are principally those of the administration of the Act. Language used is distancing (Example 2). There is some correspondence from families (Examples 4a and 4b) and, very rarely, from 'defectives' (Example 4c).

Details of daily life at home or in institutions: there are rare glimpses of the lives of certified defectives and their families (see Example 3), but on the whole the archives do not permit construction of a picture of daily life.

Policies and Personalities: it was not possible to identify any personalities who shaped the way policy was made or implemented, nor to contextualise the Committee's work in the broader politics of the country. Thus the reasons for Bedfordshire's slow implementation of the Act, in comparison with Somerset, are unclear from the county's Mental Deficiency Committee papers. A historian would have to do a lot more work on local politics to understand how the committee fitted in.

Debates and disagreements over policy: the picture I got from my study of the Committee's papers was one of remarkable unanimity in the operation and implementation of policy. I cannot conclude from this that there were no disagreements over fundamentals. For example, in 1938 the Clerk received a letter from Southampton canvassing support for compulsory sterilisation of defectives. The Clerk replied that the Committee had decided to take no action, but there are no details as to how this decision was reached or what discussion took place.

Public perceptions of the work of the Committee: one enters an enclosed world when reading these files. Whether the work of the Committee was of any interest to the wider public, or to other public bodies, is unclear. There are exceptions: there is correspondence from Poor Law Boards of Guardians, the Courts and Education Committees, all of whom had official business with the Committee. It would be necessary to examine other sources - County Council minutes, newspapers, Education Committee papers - to put the work of the Committee in a broader social and political context.

How does Bedfordshire compare with other County Record Offices?

Knowledge of this is patchy at present, but some examples are available.

- Northamptonshire Record Office holdings include: Letter Books relating to mental deficiency 1914-1938 (6 Volumes); Committee for the Care of the Mentally Defective Minutes Book 1914-1948; files re Welfare of Defectives 1913-1949.

- Information on the holdings of Cheshire Record Office will be found in Mark Jackson's chapter.

- Greater London Record Office holds individual patient files. Access to these is restricted until 80 or 100 years after the final entry, unless a special case is made.

- Norfolk Record Office holdings include Norfolk County Council Mental Deficiency Act's Committee Minutes; Minutes of the Norwich City Council Committee for the Care of the Mentally Defective (later called the Mental Treatment Committee); and the Minutes of several Mental Deficiency Special Sub-committees relating to Hostels and former Poor Law Institutions, for example, the Mental Treatment Ladies' Sub-committee. All these records are open, although one group of Special Reports on a Hostel is closed until 1999.

Conclusion

Bedfordshire's Mental Deficiency records are rich and informative. I have only touched the surface of what is possible. The remaining tasks are to complete the analysis of Bedfordshire's records; set them in the broad context of local and national politics and to compare these records with those held in other county record offices. Whilst an individual county's records can provide a good deal of insight, it is important to set them in a broader context. This is well illustrated when Bedfordshire's experience is compared to that of another southern rural county, Somerset, in the next chapter of this book.

Notes

1. Board of Control *Annual Report* 1927

2. Board of Control *Annual Report* 1937

Chapter 9

Learning from Local History: Evidence from Somerset

Dorothy Atkinson

Summary

In this chapter Dorothy Atkinson shows how she used local records from the early twentieth century, kept in the Somerset Record Office, to shed light on developments in service provision for 'mental defectives' in the county. She also uses these records to explain how Somerset, a rural county, established a range of institutions and systems which put it high on the Board of Control's 'league table' of local authorities. This chapter shows how much there is to learn from local history and demonstrates how even a modest historical quest can uncover valuable evidence about the past.

Introduction

My visits to the Somerset County Record Office in Taunton were spread over five days in the summer of 1977. Those five long days of solitary reading and pencil note-taking have themselves become historical events. Newly appointed as social worker to two small, geographically close, learning disability (or 'mental handicap', as they were then) institutions, I was curious about their origins. In the mid-seventies institutional care was still widespread but I was interested in those two hospitals particularly because they were former Poor Law Institutions. Nearly twenty years ago there was general acceptance of institutional care, and I was part of that system. But still, I wanted to know, by what turn of events had these two rather forbidding-looking institutions become residential settings for people with learning difficulties?

I pored over boxes of minutes, reports, letters, and memoranda, and read through report books and ledgers, making copious notes. My self-assigned task in the 1970s was to find out more about how and why Selwood Hospital in Frome and Norah Fry Hospital only 12 miles away in Shepton Mallet had come into being. Twenty years ago there was no audience for this knowledge, and those handwritten pencil notes remained undisturbed until the mid-1990s. The growth of interest in history, and the subsequent development of this book, have prompted their retrieval. This chapter provides a long-awaited opportunity to present some of my findings. In so doing, I hope to illustrate what riches are to be found in county record offices.

In the preceding chapter, Jan Walmsley describes the work she has done more recently in the Bedfordshire County Record Office. One of the striking features in her findings is the contrast between the two counties in their earlier residential provision for people with learning difficulties. She takes 1926 as an example, highlighting the fact that, by then, Somerset was already providing residential care and statutory supervision on a large scale whereas Bedfordshire had made provision for only modest numbers. Ostensibly the two counties seemed to have much in common in that both were predominantly rural and had few large centres of population. So why then was there this difference? What had happened, in Somerset, to put that county so far in front in terms of its 'ascertainment' rate and its provision of services?

Although the 1908 *Report of the Royal Commission on the Care and Control of the Feeble-Minded* and the 1929 *Wood Report*[1] had noted some regional variations in the level of 'mental deficiency', these tended to be disregarded for planning purposes in favour of an estimated average number of 'mental defectives' per 1000 population. Whether or not there was any real difference in the actual number of 'mental defectives' in the two counties, clearly there was a difference between them in the number of people ascertained as 'mentally deficient'. One possible explanation is that Somerset was a relatively prosperous county and in a better position, therefore, to identify and provide for a larger number of mental defectives[2]. The differences between the two counties persisted over the years. In Chapter 8, Jan Walmsley also highlights the difference in position of the two counties in the Board of Control's 'league tables' for 1937 - Somerset is near the top, Bedfordshire is near the bottom.

Could my notes, made nearly twenty years ago, begin to explain these differences? The search was on - to find those notes, to re-read and re-evaluate them and to construct at least the beginnings of an explanation. The answer to why Somerset was so 'in advance' of Bedfordshire in 1926 seemed to be that the former county had started to make its residential and supervisory provisions many years beforehand. By 1926 it already had a network of institutions, of which those in Frome and Shepton Mallet (the objects of my earlier interest) were a firmly established part. What follows in the rest of this chapter is a first attempt at reconstructing an account of how, and when, that network of institutions began, and became established in Somerset in the early years of this century. (A full list of sources is included as an appendix to this paper.)

The early years, 1900-1913

In 1900, mental defectives in Somerset were dealt with in three ways; through outdoor relief or by admission to lunatic asylums or workhouses. The two institutions of particular interest in my personal quest were former workhouses, and early records show that, in Somerset at least, workhouses played a major part in the care of mental defectives. This was not thought to be a satisfactory state of affairs and by 1900 there was already considerable concern that no proper provision existed for mental defectives. In 1900, a report was prepared by one of the Somerset Boards of Guardians and circulated to other Boards with a view to pressurising the County Council to take action[3]. The document suggested that 'with training especially adapted to their needs these patients may, in many cases, obtain a power of partial self support and be prevented from lapsing into that hopeless condition which is the result of our present system'.

The document stated that in Somerset there were some 420 'idiots' (the terminology of the time) currently known to the authorities, not counting those residing in the lunatic asylums. Of those 420 known cases, 217 were at the time living in workhouses and the other 203 were being cared for by friends and family. There was concern about those people living in the workhouses, and the general lack of special provision which meant that mental defectives had to be admitted to such institutions. A justice of the peace writing on the subject in 1900 expressed this view: 'many of the Adults of this class now in our Workhouses may possibly never have been there at all had they in early life received some specific training in developing their mental capacities.... '[4].

The recommendation made by the Boards of Guardians to Somerset County Council was that the latter should establish a separate asylum for the 'idiot paupers of the County'. It was empowered to do so, apparently, under Section 241 of the 1890 Lunacy Act. Indeed, Boards of Guardians acting alone, or in combination, could similarly set aside separate provision for this group under Section 8 of the 1879 Poor Law Act.

The Workhouse in Frome

The County Council's response was to appoint a Committee in 1901 to consider the 'Question of the Care of Idiots and Imbeciles'. The Committee reported in 1902. The report argued in favour of separate specialist provision away from the present workhouses as 'imbeciles and idiots are a source of discomfort to themselves and the other inmates'. It was felt that with a separate institution the people concerned could be trained in work, and might, therefore, become partially if not wholly self supporting thus, in the long run, saving the County money.

However, this move towards separate institutional provision did not proceed much further. The Committee sent questionnaires to the Somerset Boards of Guardians to ascertain their views. In the event, only eight supported having a separate central asylum; six were against the idea and three were undecided.

Those against the idea included the Temple Cloud Board of Guardians, who felt that a central large institution miles away in Taunton would be harmful to their local 'defectives' who would be obliged to move away from their family and friends. Frome Guardians also opposed the idea on the grounds that they already had specialist wards and special attendants in their workhouse to care for their own local 'defectives'.

Indeed the Frome Poor Law Institution (which later became Selwood Hospital) had been dealing with 'idiots' and 'imbeciles' at least since the passing of the 1890 Lunacy Act. In 1891, the Visiting Committee for Imbeciles noted that the institution was then caring for 17 male 'imbeciles' and 19 female 'imbeciles'. The Guardians were appointing specialist staff to care for them, as illustrated by the advertisement which appeared on 3rd April, 1900:

Male and Female Attendant
for the Imbeciles at the Workhouse

Salary
Male Attendant   £22 per annum
Female Attendant   £20 per annum,

and usual Officers' Rations, Apartments and Washing;
also an Allowance in Money in lieu of Beer if desired

Man and Wife, without encumbrance, who have had
experience in the care of the Insane, preferred

At the time of the Committee's report in 1902, Frome was accommodating five idiots, 15 male imbeciles and 15 female imbeciles.

The local concern with how to provide for mental defectives reflected a growing national concern. In 1904, the Royal Commission on the Care and Control of the Feeble-Minded was set up. It reported in 1908, its recommendations forming the basis of the 1913 Mental Deficiency Act.

In Somerset, meanwhile, interest in the subject also remained high. In 1910, at a conference in Taunton, the Poor Law Guardians formally approved the principle: 'That imbeciles, epileptics and idiots should be isolated under proper supervision', and recommended that a joint committee, consisting of several unions, be set up to co-ordinate action on that principle. The proposal was backed by the information that: 'of the 17 Union Workhouses in Somerset, only Bath and Frome Unions provide for the treatment and accommodation of Imbeciles and Idiots by housing the patients in separate quarters in the care of qualified attendants'[6]. A joint committee, as proposed by the conference delegates, was formed in 1911.

A memorandum from a certain Robert Bluford in 1911 made the point that 'one or more Workhouses in Somerset should be given up, as far as possible, to the reception of Imbeciles etc. from within the area'. The County Council stated, in 1911, that an estimated 106 'certified or certifiable imbeciles etc.,' were currently living in workhouses and would need a separate institution[7]. The Taunton Guardians were interested in giving up their workhouse for this purpose, as were the Temple Cloud Guardians but the Frome Guardians replied, again, that they already had their own facilities. In fact the scheme faltered through long disputes between the different Boards about terms and costs and, for a second time, co-ordinated action to provide for mental defectives failed to get off the ground[8].

On the 11th November, 1911, a Conference Paper entitled 'The Problem of the Feeble-Minded' was delivered to an audience in Somerset. The paper argued, in keeping with the prevailing views of the time, that 'mental defectives' were increasing their numbers rapidly, that they were responsible for, or involved in, most of the social evils of the time, and that the solution was their permanent segregation in institutions. In the words of the paper: 'The extent of the danger to the community caused by the presence of these degenerate persons in its midst cannot be clearly estimated. Workhouses, prisons, inebriate and penitentiary homes are largely peopled by them and their progeny'.

The paper quotes from the findings of the Royal Commission's Medical Expert[9], who had visited six of the 17 Somerset Union areas. Apparently, he had established that there were 916 mental defectives in total, of whom 447 were unsuitably provided for, or not provided for at all. The figure 447 was further broken down into 165 feeble-minded women, two fifths of whom had given birth to children (two thirds of the offspring being illegitimate) and 312 mental defectives 'entirely or partially supported by the public purse'. The paper urged that the public be awakened to the danger of allowing the multiplication of the feeble-minded to continue unchecked, and that institutions be established for 'the care and improvement' of the feeble-minded; institutions which would 'promote their happiness' while providing for their permanent detention.

In 1912, the South West Counties Association for the Permanent Care of the Feeble-Minded was founded. The association's aims included:

- to check the procreation of feeble-minded persons

- to relieve pressure on the lunatic asylums, workhouses and the rates

- to render the lives of the feeble-minded as useful and happy as circumstances will permit.

The association also aimed to set up a Feeble-Minded Colony to offer care and training, and was appealing for funds for this purpose.

The Appeal for Funds stressed that there was a steady increase in the number of feeble-minded people every year, and that 'the rate of increase of such persons is, in proportion, if not checked, more rapid than that of persons of sound mind'. The 'weakness of mind is hereditary' so, it was argued, the increase in the number of 'mental defectives' was inevitable. 'Some of them find their way into asylums where they are maintained at a needlessly large cost, others are to be found in Workhouses where they are unfit and undesirable companions for the other inmates'. However, the association's greatest concern was with the majority of mental defectives who were 'at large'. These people were described as 'a burden and a danger to those among whom they live, who are unable to provide for them the constant vigilance and control which is needed for the protection both of the persons themselves and those around them'[10]

Meanwhile the Workhouses continued to provide for the mental defectives that came to their notice. Frome Workhouse was now noted for its specialist facilities and staff, and received requests from other unions for help with specific cases. In 1911, the Clutton Board of Guardians approached the Frome Guardians to see if they could accommodate 'imbeciles and weak minded patients' from the Clutton area. The Frome Workhouse then had 41 beds (20 male, 21 female) set aside for mental defectives, although only 31 were then occupied[11]. In 1912, the Chard Board of Guardians referred two girls to Frome. They had recently returned from Starcross (in Devon); one of them was said to be 'unimprovable', and both of them were considered unsuitable either for an asylum or 'an ordinary Workhouse'[12] The Frome Workhouse would have increased its number of mental defectives further except for its shortage of night attendants. The Master of the Workhouse wrote at the time: 'The patients have to be left by night in charge of able-bodied inmates, which is very unsatisfactory, and has been a great source of worry and anxiety to me'.[13]

A network of institutions, 1913 to 1929

The Mental Deficiency Act was passed in 1913. It set the scene for the further development of the two institutions which were of special interest to me in my original quest - but it also set the scene for the network of institutions which were to form the basis of 'care' for mental defectives in Somerset for many years to come. The Act established a central Board of Control, required a Mental Deficiency Committee to be set up in each county, and set out methods of disposal for those people coming to the notice of the local authority. The methods of disposal included guardianship and licence from the institution, as well as institutional care. Although the Act provided for the permanent care of mental defectives in segregated institutions, it also allowed many others to live in the community.

In Somerset, the Mental Deficiency Act Committee was duly formed, chaired for many years by Miss Norah Fry (later Mrs Cooke-Hurle) whose name was later given to the institution at Shepton Mallet. The account which follows has been largely constructed from the minutes of that Committee.

The Frome Workhouse (later Selwood Hospital) still catered for mental defectives in wards set aside for that purpose. In a similar way, the Long Ashton Workhouse (later Farleigh Hospital) was catering for small numbers, and in the years 1917-1920 accommodated 16 mental defectives, ten men and six women. And the Shepton Mallet Workhouse (later Norah Fry Hospital) accommodated 19 mental defectives in the years 1918-1922. By 1918, Somerset's network of institutions for the care of mental defectives was almost in place (Table 1).

Table 9.1

INSTITUTIONAL PROVISION IN SOMERSET, 1918

1918   In addition to the Frome Workhouse, the following institutions appear on the Board of Control's Lists of that year:

List of Certified Institutions
Entry 44   Somerset County
                 Council   Yatton Hall, Yatton

                 Managers/owners -   Somerset Association for the
                                     Care of the Mentally Deficient

35 mental defectives of both sexes.

List of Institutions Approved under Section 37
Entry 55   Somerset   Imbecile Wards,
                                        Long Ashton Poor Law
                                        Institution, Flax Bourton, Bristol.
                 10 male, 6 female defectives

Entry 56   Somerset   Poor Law Institution
                                        Shepton Mallet

3 male, 16 female adult defectives

(*Source*: Board of Control's List of Certified Institutions 1918)

The Board of Control was reluctant to approve workhouses as suitable institutions for the care of mental defectives, preferring the development of large specialist colonies which would properly provide care and training for larger numbers away from the influence of other types of inmates. Nevertheless, the Somerset Mental Deficiency Committee made strenuous efforts to gain recognition for the Long Ashton and Shepton Mallet institutions whilst awaiting the setting up of a colony of the prescribed type in the county. Its efforts were rewarded, and in 1922 the two institutions were approved under Section 37 of the Act. The Long Ashton institution was approved to cater for 66 mental defectives (32 men, 34 women) and the Shepton Mallet institution could expand to 28 mental defectives (3 men, 25 women).

What was life like for the inmates in those early institutions? Some glimpses are revealed in correspondence between the Mental Deficiency Committee and other public authorities. Two short extracts are included below, both taken from letters written in 1922 and referring to Shepton Mallet Poor Law Institution.

....The number of patients at present is two male and 17 female. Separate day rooms and dormitories have been provided for the female defectives, and they have their own officer. They are employed in the laundry and in the domestic work of the Institution. They are neatly dressed and are given different clothing to the pauper inmates. They are taken out for walks regularly and adequate arrangements have been made for indoor recreation. As the number of male defectives is so small, no special arrangements have been made by the Committee, but the Master himself makes suitable provision for their recreation and training
(Extract from letter, 31st July, 1922: Mental Deficiency
Committee to Somerset County Council)

..Separate wards have also been set apart at Shepton Mallet which is certified for 25 female and three male defectives. The female defectives sent to this Institution consist almost entirely of young women who have given birth to illegitimate children
(Extract from letter, 29th August, 1922: Mental Deficiency
Committee to Frome Guardians)

Meanwhile, Yatton Hall was established by the Somerset Association for the Care of the Mentally Defective as a Certified Institution for the Care of Defectives. In 1918 Yatton Hall had accommodation for 35 mental defectives of both sexes, 31 of these being 'low grade' children under 16, and four of these 'high grade' young women, aged 16-20, who would help mind the children and run the institution. (They later became known as The Service Girls.) In 1919, Yatton Hall was handed over to Somerset County Council and, in 1922, was recognised by the Board of Control as a suitable institution for the care of mental defectives. It was permitted to accommodate 76 patients.

The network of provision was not yet complete, however. Apart from Yatton Hall, institutional provision in the early 1920s was entirely located in the old workhouses. The Mental Deficiency Committee decided, therefore, to acquire land and premises for the development of a colony for the feeble-minded. Its proposed site was a mansion, built in 1820 and known as Sandhill Park. This was set in 130 acres of land just outside Taunton near the village of Bishops Lydeard. The acquisition of Sandhill Park was approved for the purpose by the Minister of Health in 1921. The approved plan was to use the mansion to house 72 adult females and 40 girls under the age of 16; to set up hutments for 40 boys; and to establish a Special Residential School for 80 children (40 boys, 40 girls).

In 1922, the Committee described their proposal thus:

> The Committee have a scheme for providing a Farm Colony at Sandhill Park, near Bishops Lydeard, but the defectives to be accommodated there are children and young women who are trainable in habits and handicrafts or remunerative employment. It is not intended to provide accommodation for young women of immoral tendencies, or for low grade adult defectives. The Committee are quite satisfied that they can be properly looked after in special wards of the Poor Law Institutions....
>
> *(Extract from letter, 29th August 1922: Mental Deficiency Committee to Frome Guardians)*

In 1925, staff were appointed to the Colony, as follows:

Superintendent, a female	} 'both Spinsters'
Principal Teacher, a female	
Assistant Superintendent	£80 per annum
Cook Matron	£60 per annum
One Teacher Attendant	} £35 per person
Four Nurse Attendants	per annum

The Colony opened its doors on 23rd September, 1925, admitting in the first instance, '72 feeble-minded girls and young women in need of care and training'. The network of institutional provision was in place by 1925; it consisted of Sandhill Park Colony, Yatton Hall and the three Poor Law Institutions at Frome, Shepton Mallet and Long Ashton. The figures in Table 2 show a relatively steep increase in overall numbers catered for in institutions in Somerset in 1926, reflecting the intake of a new group of inmates into the system in the previous year.

Matron of Shepton Mallet workhouse

Master of Shepton Mallet workhouse

Norah Fry Hospital prior to closure in 1993

Table 9.2

SOMERSET COUNTY STATISTICS

	Institutions	Guardianship	Supervision by Somerset Association for Mental Welfare	Licence
1924	294	15	930	
1925	316	23	972	
1926	399	22	1131	
1927	458	30	1134	45
1928	457	37	1128	39
1929	475	41	1109	48

(*Source*: Mental Deficiency Committee Minutes)

In 1926, the Board of Control, still unhappy with the continuing use of Poor Law premises for the care of mental defectives, and giving approval for specified periods and specified numbers only, now suggested to the Committee that Sandhill Park Colony should be developed for all classes and both sexes of mental defectives. The Board said that the Poor Law Institutions were 'not suitable for the permanent accommodation of Mental Defectives, as such accommodation does not afford facilities for their proper classification, occupation and recreation'. The Committee refused, partly on the grounds that the conditions of the benefactor included the specification that Sandhill Park be used for 'high grade' patients, but also because its members preferred to see the expansion of the Poor Law premises to take the 'low grade' patients.[14]

As Table 2 illustrates, many mental defectives were, at this time, being dealt with in the community, as the Mental Deficiency Act had intended. The thirteenth Annual Report of the Somerset Association for Mental Welfare was published in 1927. It listed '212 cases' that it was dealing with under Statutory Supervision and '917 cases' under Voluntary Supervision. The Report stated:

> ...It is clearly impossible, even if it were desirable, to provide institutional care for all our defectives, so that there must necessarily be a considerable proportion left in the care of their

relatives for whom the Association are required to provide supervision. All mental defectives need care and control for their own protection, or for the protection of others, and for the majority this can only be provided satisfactorily in an Institution, but supervision, if properly carried out, may postpone the necessity for removal to an Institution. Supervision is simply a means of preventive care for the less urgent cases...

As well as preventive work, the Somerset Association was interested in following up those mental defectives who had received some institutional training, suggesting that such training was beneficial to the defectives concerned. In the same annual report the Association made this point:

> ...Experience has proved that defectives are much more likely to succeed under Guardianship or Supervision after they have received a period of training at a Residential Special School, or an Institution, in good habits, self control, obedience and in some trade or occupation. The County Mental Deficiency Act Committee have placed 45 mental defectives out on licence from Institutions, and only 11 have been recalled...

Whatever the virtues and benefits of supervision, the number of mental defectives being certified and placed in institutions was steadily growing. In 1928, the total for the county was 457 (compared with 294 in 1924 - see Table 2). In that year, Yatton Hall accommodated 75 defectives, Long Ashton accommodated 66, Shepton Mallet accommodated 56 and Frome was approved by Board of Control and Ministry Inspectors, for a three year period, to open another ward for a further 16 defectives. The approval for the Frome expansion was conditional on the carrying out of some minor alterations and the appointment of additional nursing staff.

The Board of Control was still not happy with the continuing confinement of mental defectives in 'the barrack buildings' of the Poor Law Institutions. The stated preference was for the development of 'proper and adequate accommodation in colonies'[15] Thus, in 1928 Sandhill Park Colony was able to expand its numbers to 105 (60 young women, 45 school children). The network of institutions was now in place and fully operational.

Conclusion

My original quest in 1977 was to use county records to trace the origins and later development of the two learning disability hospitals in which I was then engaged as a social worker. They were former work-houses. How had they first become involved in this work? There was no neat history of these two institutions which I could refer to. Instead, I had to piece together the story of their involvement in the care of 'mental defectives'. Inevitably it turned out to be a complicated story. The two institutions were in fact relatively minor players in a complex national and regional system set up to care for and control people with learning difficulties. In tracing their history, it has been necessary to include the inter-connecting stories of the other institutions in Somerset.

The reconstruction of this history from documents in the county record office has also shed light on the question which this chapter set out to answer. Why was there such a disparity in institutional and supervisory provisions between the two rural counties of Bedfordshire and Somerset in the 1920s? The reason for Somerset's 'pre-eminence' in this respect seemed to be that it took an early interest in, and began making provision for, those mental defectives which came to the notice of its public authorities. By 1926, the year of the disparity in numbers high-lighted by Jan Walmsley in Chapter 8, the county already had in place the network of institutions which were to provide residential care for the next fifty years.

But *why* had the county made its early start? As this chapter has shown, the answer seems to lie with the interest shown by various Boards of Guardians at the turn of the century (and before), in the welfare of mental defectives, and in the provision they increasingly made available for them in certain workhouses. Tracing the history of two of these ex-workhouses was my first quest. In doing so, I found that they were among the last surviving remnants of that network of institutions which had held sway in Somerset for so many years - and which, between them, had put the county high in the Board of Control's 'league tables' in the 1920s. This seems to provide the explanation I sought in my second quest.

One interesting postscript is that although Somerset in the early years of this century was quick to establish its institutional provision, those institutions were closed some years ago. By way of contrast, Bedfordshire was late to start providing institutional care but the institution it finally established is still open at the time of writing (albeit in different hands at the end of the century).

Notes

1. *Report of the Mental Deficiency Committee* Chairman: A. Wood (HMSO, 1929).

2. Mathew Thomson looks at geographical factors in *The Problem of Mental Deficiency in England and Wales, 1913-1946* (Unpublished D.Phil. thesis, Oxford, 1992).

3. *Report on the Care of Idiots* (1900). Somerset Boards of Guardians.

4. This view was expressed in a JP's letter, dated 19th May, 1900, filed with the Boards of Guardians' papers.

5. This information is contained in a committee appointed by Somerset County Council: *The Care of Imbeciles and Idiots* (1902).

6. These quotes are taken from the report of the conference of Poor Law Guardian Delegates held in Taunton in 1910.

7. This information comes from the Somerset Council papers on the Combination of Guardians, November 1911.

8. These points were made in correspondence between Boards of Guardians on the subject of the care of imbeciles.

9. This refers to the *Report of the Royal Commission on the Care and Control of the Feeble-Minded*, Chairman: Lord Radnor (Cmnd 420, HMSO, 1908).

10. These quotes are taken from the South Western Counties' Association for the Care of the Feeble-Minded's *Appeal for Funds to Establish a Feeble-Minded Colony*, 1912.

11. Report on *Imbecile Accommodation at Frome Union Workhouse,* December 1911.

12. Correspondence between Boards of Guardians.

13. Tapp, the Master of Frome Workhouse, is quoted thus in the *Report on Imbecile Accommodation* (see note 11).

14. This information is recorded in the minutes of the Mental Deficiency Committee, June, 1926.

15. These quotes are taken from the report of the Deputation to the Board of Control, 1927 (filed with the MDC minutes for that year).

Appendix

Somerset County Records

1 EARLY RECORDS OF TWO INSTITUTIONS

Frome Union Records [DIG/F] (Frome Workhouse later became Selwood Hospital).
* Admissions and Discharge Books from 1847 (Vol I onwards) [60/1-37]
* Visiting Committee for Lunatics, 1890-94 [99b/1]
* Relieving Officer, Application and Report Book, Frome District; 1837-38, 1911-12 [134/1-8, 14-15]
* Boarded Out Children, Reports 1914-26 [41/1]
* Regulations for Conduct of the Workhouse, 1914 [3/1]
* Imbecile Accommodation at Frome Union Workhouse, 1911.

Shepton Mallet Union Records [DIG/SM] (Shepton Mallet Workhouse later became Norah Fry Hospital).
* Admissions and Discharges, 1853-55 [60/1]
* Certificates for the Detention of Lunatics, 1888-89 [75b/1]
* Register of Mechanical Restraints, 1897-1922 [75c/1]
* Relieving Officer, Application and Report Book, District 1; 1838, 1911-12 [134/1,4]
* Lady Visitors' Report Book, 1900-22 [99c/1]
* Boarded Out Children, Reports 1903-10 [43/1]
* General Visiting Committee Report Book, 1904-27 [99a/1]

2 PAPERS FROM THE BOARDS OF GUARDIANS
* Report on the Care of Idiots, Somerset Boards of Guardians, 1900
* JP's letter, 1900
* Care of Imbeciles and Idiots: a report by a Committee appointed by Somerset County Council, 1902
* Report of a Conference of Poor Law Guardians Delegates in Taunton, 1910
* Memorandum from Robert Burford, 1911
* Correspondence between Boards of Guardians on the subject of Care of Imbeciles: e.g. Frome and Temple Cloud Boards, 1912; Frome and Clutton Boards, 1912
* Report from Devizes Union, 1912
* Letter from Mental Deficiency Act Committee to Frome Clerk, 1922

* Letter from the Clerk to the Frome Guardians to the Ministry of Health, 1927
* List of Certified Institutions in Somerset, 1918.

3 **CAMPAIGN AND COLONY PAPERS** (a collection of national and local papers).
* Report by the National Association for Promoting the Welfare of the Feeble-Minded, 1908 [C/CHIMD/2/22]
* Conference Paper, 'The Problem of the Feeble-Minded', delivered in Somerset, 11th November, 1911 [C/CR1MD/2/28]
* Letter from Miss Norah Fry, on behalf of the South West Counties Association for the Permanent Care of the FeebleMinded, 1912
* South West Counties Association, Appeal for Funds to establish a Feeble-Minded Colony, 1912
* The Joint Committee in Support of the Mental Deficiency Bill 1908-1912, various papers:
  'The Mental Deficiency Bill must be passed Without Delay.'
  'Liberty, some examples of what is being done in its name.'
  'The Existing Evils.'
* Letter from the Central Association for the Care of the Mentally Deficient, 1917
* Board of Control Memoranda, 1921, 1922.

4 **MENTAL DEFICIENCY ACT COMMITTEE MINUTES AND PAPERS**
* Reports of the Somerset Mental Deficiency Act Committee, 1917-44 [C/MD/1/13]
* Somerset Mental Deficiency Act Committee Minutes, 1925-27 [C/MD/4/29]
* Agreements with other Authorities and Institutions for the Acceptance of Mental Defectives, 1919-47 [C/MD/1/3]
* Thirteenth Annual Report of the Somerset Association for Mental Welfare, 1927 [C/MD/1/16]
* Specimen Agreement for the Reception of Mentally Defective Persons [C/MD/1/15]
* Annual Report of the Court of Quarter Sessions of Visitors of and Institutions for, Mental Defectives, 1943 [C/MD/1/6].

Chapter 10

Collections in the Wellcome Institute for the History of Medicine

Julia Sheppard

Summary

The Library of the Wellcome Institute for the History of Medicine is an important repository for documents relating to the history of medicine. Here Julia Sheppard, Archivist in the Contemporary Medical Archives Centre (CMAC), shows how the collection can be used for exploring the history of learning disability.

Introduction

The Wellcome Institute holds a great deal of material of interest to those interested in the history of disability which can be studied to reveal the treatment and attitudes towards people suffering from mental or physical disabilities. This chapter seeks to advise readers on how to make use of the collection.

Using the collection

Anyone wishing to study the history of people with learning disabilities will need to be aware of the following points:

1   That they will need to use historical vocabulary and not be shocked by it. One of the major problems when visiting a historical library like the Wellcome Institute is to remember that the catalogues, indexes and lists will, in all probability, employ historical vocabulary, and it will be necessary to explore these using the original terminology applied, such as 'mentally defective/mentally deficient/idiot/backward/mongol/cretin/feeble-minded', etc.

2   They will need to think around the subject. Archives are not normally arranged on a subject basis and do not necessarily have indexes. It may be that papers of an individual may emerge in the records of an organisation (of which they may be an officer, member or simply a correspondent). Alternatively, stray records of some organisations appear in the collections of papers of individuals. There is more in libraries and archive repositories than appears at first sight.

3   The experience of the patient in large institutions is not normally recorded in the official records of that institution and, to some extent is therefore lost to historians. This is where oral history has a great deal to offer in documenting people's lives.

4   Finally, bear in mind that some of the material is likely to be sensitive. Patient records are not normally made available if less than 100 years old (75 years for Scotland) and it is at the discretion of the health authorities concerned to allow access. Archivists and historians are conscious of the need to respect confidentiality, whilst at the same time trying to make some material available where adequate protection is given to individuals. In the CMAC an undertaking must be signed which sets out that certain conditions must be observed. Ministry of Health guidance HC (89) 20 and in Scotland MEL (1993)152 discusses these issues.

The collection is also a starting point for locating archives held else-where. There are two surveys run by the Institute which will yield information on such sources:

The Hospital Records Project, run jointly with the Public Record Office, is a database of information on the location and main categories of the records of more than 2000 hospitals throughout the UK. The vast majority of these records are deposited in local authority record offices which will hold more detailed information on them.

The Retreat, and the Colney Hatch Asylum, are just two of the hospitals about whose records information is held, but the database can also be queried with an overall search. It reveals, for example, that there are about 201 entries on pre 1948 mental hospitals and 225 entries on post-1948 mental and psychiatric hospitals.

The Medical Archives and Manuscripts Survey 1660-1945 is also maintained at the Wellcome Institute. Information continues to be gathered from a large number of libraries, medical societies, charities and other organisations. It is intended that this will eventually be published, but in the meantime, print-outs of the entries are available for consultation at the Library.

Leaving aside the library's book and reprint material in the Historical and Modern Medicine collections, there are several other departments in the library. It is worth consulting the **Iconographic Department** holdings for images of disability. These include, for example, photographs of patients collected by G.E. Shuttleworth (author of *Mentally Deficient Children 1895*), especially people with Down's Syndrome and asylum inmates (ref: ICV 30486-30542), and can be viewed on the Department's Video-disc Project. Films, such as *Out of Sight* (Channel 4 BBC 2 1992) or the BUFVC *Diagnosis of Imbecility* (1957 with a 24 year follow up in 1981) may be viewed there. Some are available for hire or purchase from the **Wellcome Centre** (also in the Wellcome Building). A full catalogue is available.

The Western Manuscripts Department has a large collection of the papers of G.E. Shuttleworth which presumably arrived with the photographs mentioned above, as well as papers of Albert Wilson, Medical Superintendent of the Essex County Asylum, Walthamstow, covering the period 1873-1912.

Photograph of two boys from the Shuttleworth Collection (Wellcome Institute Library).

In the **Contemporary Medical Archives Centre** there are several collections, both of papers of individuals and archives of organisations, which contain material of potential interest in this field.

The Eugenics Society, founded in 1907, became involved in the issue of so called 'problem families' as well as corresponding with organisations such as the National Association for Mental Health, the National Society for Lunacy Reform, and the National Workers Committee for the Legalising of Voluntary Sterilisation. The Society campaigned for voluntary sterilisation, sought to educate the public about inherited defects, and accumulated family pedigrees, histories and photographs and literature about the 'feeble-minded'. It proposed the Feeble-Minded Control Bill, and the archive includes correspondence from its members about the bill, one for example suggesting that those with tuberculosis should also not be allowed to reproduce.

The medical profession as a whole was also concerned about these issues, and there are files on the issue of sterilisation in the archives of the British Medical Association. The indexed list has many entries under 'Mental' (certification under the Mental Deficiency Acts/mental health services of local authorities etc). There are three files of papers, evidence and final report of the Mental Deficiency Committee 1931-2. Correspondence of the BMA of interest will also be found under other subject headings: the Infantile Paralysis Fellowship; Deafness/the Disability Persons Act/welfare of the blind and so on. These files cover varying dates, mainly for the period 1910-1950, and the BMA retains some of its later files.

The archive of the Association of County Medical Officers of Health includes documents from the 1960s on the care and teaching of mentally handicapped children. The training of staff of training centres for the mentally subnormal is discussed by Medical Officers of Health and it chronicles the shift in attitudes that such children should be encouraged and motivated rather than merely given basket-work type activities.

The Family Planning Association may not be an obvious archive to consult, but it did concern itself with domiciliary birth control in cases where the woman was unable to attend a clinic. There was an obvious overlap with issues of family welfare and 'problem families'. The records include information on the 1957 Mental Health Exhibition with which it was involved 'mainly to allay prejudice and fear of the public to mental illness and treatment, especially hospitalisation'.

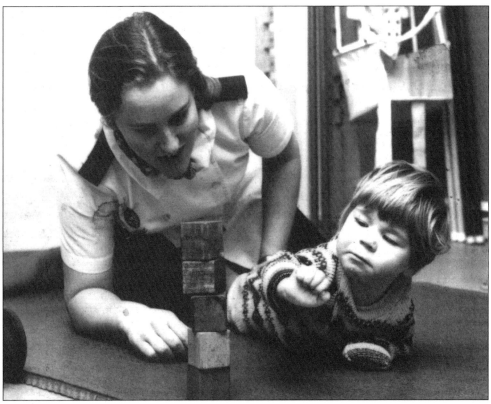

'Guided play': Photograph from the records of the Chartered Society of Physiotherapy (Wellcome Institute Library)

Other professional bodies, including the Association of Health and Residential Care Officers (AHRCO), the Health Visitors Association (HVA) and the Mental Aftercare Association (MACA), have placed their archives in the CMAC. The latter is a recent accession and is to be catalogued in the near future. It is worth remembering that these bodies also corresponded with others of relevance; AHRCO's records include correspondence with the National Association for Mental Health, 1965-74.

Individuals contributed to committee work or carried out their own research as well, and the papers, lecture notes, correspondence and case notes in several other collections will also be relevant.

The psychiatrist Noel Harris (1897-1963) worked at both St Luke's and the Middlesex Hospital and his papers include notes and reprints on epilepsy and correspondence on the relationship between tuberculosis and mental diseases. Poems, notes and drawings by his patients (including two cat pictures by Louis Wain) are also in the collection.

Professor Donald Hunter (1898-1979) worked for much of his life at the London Hospital and studied occupational health. His case notes and photographs include examples of mongols and dwarfism, and remind us that an individual's physical appearance could lead to the automatic assumption that they were stupid. Other personal papers likely to include material of relevance to this topic are the papers of Frederick Parkes Weber (1863-1962), a specialist in rare disease; and Melanie Klein (1882-1960) and John Bowlby (1907-1990), eminent psychoanalysts.[1]

Conclusion

This chapter set out to give practical advice to anyone interested in piecing together the history of learning disability using sources held in a major archive. The advice given here should hold good for other such archive searches. The title of this book, *Forgotten Lives,* is a reminder that the would-be historian will not find sources neatly packaged under the 'Learning Disability' label. The history is dispersed in the work of the many different specialists who have had a hand in the lives of people with learning disabilities, for better or worse. The task of piecing together the specific history of learning disability remains to be done, and will involve painstaking detective work and some historical imagination.

Note

1. The Wellcome Institute Library is open Monday, Wednesday and Friday 9.45-5.15, Tuesday and Thursday 9.45-7.15, and Saturday 9.45-1.00. Arrangements to consult the archives, manuscripts and other rare materials must be made in advance. Its address is: 183 Euston Road, London, NW1 2BE. Tel: 0171 611 8888

Bibliography

Abbott, P. and Sapsford, R. (1987) *Community Care for Mentally Handicapped Children.* Milton Keynes: Open University Press

Achenbach, P. (1967) *Mental Subnormality 1324-1961*, PhD thesis, University of Dublin

Atkinson, D. and Williams, F. (1990) *Know Me As I Am,* London: Hodder and Stoughton

Atkinson, D and Walmsley, J. (1995) A woman's place?, in T. Philpot and L. Ward (eds.). *Values and Visions,* London: Butterworth Heinemann

Atkinson, D. and Walmsley, J. (in press) Using autobiographical approaches with people with learning difficulties, *Auto / biography*

Barclay, J. (1988) *Langho Epileptic Colony 1906-1984: A Contextual Study of the Origins Transformations and Demise of Manchester Colony for Sane Pauper Epileptics,* PhD thesis, University of Manchester

Barker, D. (1985) How to curb the fertility of the unfit: the feeble minded in Edwardian Britain, *Oxford Review of Education,* 9, 197-211

Barker, D. (1989) The biology of stupidity: genetics, eugenics and mental deficiency in the inter-war years, *British Journal for the History of Science,* 22, 347-375

Barrett, M. (1986) *From Education to Segregation: An Inquiry into the Changing Character of Special Provision for the Retarded in England, 1846-1918*, PhD thesis, University of Lancaster

Bingley, R. (1995) *South Ockendon: Echoes from an Essex Hospital,* South Ockendon Hospital Publication

Bornat, J. (1993) *Reminiscence Reviewed: Perspectives, Evaluations and Achievements,* Buckingham: Open University Press

Booth, T. (1985) Labels and their consequences, in D. Lane and B. Stratford, (eds.), *Current Approaches to Down's Syndrome.,* London: Holt Rhinehart and Winston

Brechin, A. and Walmsley, J. (1989) *Making Connections: Reflecting on the Lives and Experiences of People with Learning Difficulties,* London: Hodder and Stoughton

Burleigh, M. (1994) *Death and Deliverance: Euthanasia in Germany 1900-1945,* Cambridge: Cambridge University Press

Clarke, A. M. and Clarke, A. D. B. (eds.) (1958) *Mental Deficiency: The Changing Outlook,* London: Methuen & Co

Clausen, J. (1967) Mental deficiency: development of a concept, *American Journal of Mental Deficiency,* 71, 727-745

Cole, T. (1989) *Apart or A Part? Integration and the Growth of British Special Education,* Milton Keynes: Open University Press

Crookshank, F. G. (1931) *The Mongol in Our Midst.* London 3rd ed.

Day, K. and Jancar, J. (1991) Mental handicap and the Royal Medico-Psychological Association: a historical association, 1841-1991, in G. H. Berrios and H. Freeman (eds.) *150 Years of British Psychiatry 1841-1991,* London: Gaskell

Deacon, J. (1977) *Tongue Tied,* London: National Society for Mentally Handicapped Children

Diplock, M. (1990) *The History of the Leavesden Hospital,* (private publication)

Doll, E. (1967) Trends and problems in the education of the mentally retarded 1800-1940, *American Journal of Mental Deficiency,* 72, 175-183

Donges, G. S. (1982) *Policymaking for the Mentally Handicapped,* London: Gower

Dowell, G. W. and Golden, J. (1989) Photographs as data: an analysis of images from a mental hospital, *Qualitative Sociology,* 12, 183-213

Edgerton, R. B. (1967) *The Cloak of Competence: Stigma in the Lives of the Mentally Retarded,* Berkeley: University of California Press

Farrall, L. A. (1979) The history of eugenics; a bibliographical review, *Annals of Science,* 36, 111-123

Ferguson, P. M. (1994) *Abandoned to their Fate: Social Policy and Practice Toward Severely Retarded People in America, 1820-1920,* Philadelphia: Temple University Press

Fido, R. and Potts, M. (1989) "It's not true what was written down!": experiences of life in a mental handicap institution, *Oral History,* 17, 31-34

Goffman, E. (1961) *Asylums: Essays on the Social Situation of Mental Patients and other Inmates,* New York: Anchor Books

Hirst, D. (1981) A failure "without parallel": the School Medical Service and the London County Council 1907-1912, *Medical History,* 25, 281-300

Hirst, D. (1989) The growth of treatment through the School Medical Service 1908-1918, *Medical History,* 33, 318-342

Hirst, D. (1991) Public health and the public elementary schools 1870-1907, *History of Education,* 20, 107-118

Humphries, S. and Gordon, P. (1992) *Out of Sight: The Experience of Disability 1900-1950,* Plymouth, Northgate House

Humphries, S. and Gordon, P. (1993) *Back to Your Roots: Recording Your Family History,* London: BBC Publications

Hunt, N. (1966) *The World of Nigel Hunt,* Ballater, Asset Recycling Ltd.

Hurt, J. S. (1988) *Outside the Mainstream: A History of Special Education,* London

Jackson, M. (1993) From work to therapy: the changing politics of occupation in the twentieth century, *British Journal of Occupational Therapy,* 56, 360-364

Jackson, M. (1995) Images of deviance: visual representations of mental defectives in early twentieth century medical texts, *British Journal for the History of Science,* 28, 319-337

Jackson, M. (1996) Institutional provision for the feeble-minded in Edwardian England: Sandlebridge and the scientific morality of permanent care, in D. Wright and A. Digby (eds.), *From Idiocy to Mental Deficiency: Historical Perspectives on People with Learning Disabilities,* London: Routledge

Jarvis, E. (1971) *Insanity and Idiocy in Massachussetts,* Cambridge, Harvard University Press

Jones, G. (1986) *Social Hygiene in Twentieth Century Britain,* Beckenham: Croom Helm

Jones, K. (1960) *Mental Health and Social Policy 1948-1959,* London: Routledge and Kegan Paul

Jones, K. (1972) *A History of the Mental Health Services,* London: Routledge and Kegan Paul

Jones, K. (1975) *Opening the Door: A Study of the New Policies for the Mentally Handicapped,* London: Routledge and Kegan Paul

Kanner, L. (1964) *A History of the Care and Study of the Mentally Retarded,* Illinois: Charles Thomas

Kevles, D. J. (1986) *In the Name of Eugenics,* London: Pelican

Lane, D. and Stratford, B. (eds.) (1985) *Current Approaches to Down's Syndrome,* London: Holt Reinhart and Winston

Lowe, R. A. (1979) Eugenicists, doctors and the quest for national efficiency: an educational crusade 1900-1939, *History of Education,* 8, 293-306

Luckin, B. (1983) Towards a social history of institutionalisation, *Social History,* 8, 87-94

MacNicol, J. (1983) Eugenics, medicine and mental deficiency, an introduction, *Oxford Review of Education,* 9, 177-180

MacNicol, J. (1987) In pursuit of the underclass, *Journal of Social Policy,* 16, 293-318

Malster, R. (1994) *St Lawrence's: The story of a Hospital 1870-1994,* Caterham: Lifecare NHS Trust

Matthews, F. B. (no date given) *Mental Health Services: A Handbook on Lunacy Mental Treatment and Mental Deficiency,* London: Shaw and Sons Ltd.

Morris, P. (1969) *Put Away: A Sociological Study of Institutions for the Mentally Retarded,* London: Routledge and Kegan Paul

Nolan, P. (1993) *A History of Mental Health Nursing,* London: Chapman and Hall

Noll, S. (1995) *Feeble Minded in our Midst: Institutions for the Mentally Retarded in the South 1900-1914*, University of South Carolina Press

Parry-Jones,W. L. (1981) The model of the Geel Lunatic Colony and its influence on the nineteenth century asylum system in Britain, in A. Scull (ed.) *Madhouses, Mad-Doctors and Madmen,* London: Athlone Press

Paul, D. B. (1995) *Controlling Human Heredity 1865 to the Present*, New Jersey: Humanities Press

Penrose, L. S. (1966) The contribution of mental deficiency research to psychiatry, *British Journal of Psychiatry,* 112, 747-755

Potts, M. and Fido, R. (1991) *'A Fit Person to be Removed': Personal Accounts of Life in a Mental Deficiency Institution,* Plymouth: Northcote House.

Potts, P. (1983) Medicine, morals and mental deficiency: the contribution of doctors to the development of special education in England, *Oxford Review of Education,* 9, 181-196

Potts, P. (1995) What's the use of history? Understanding educational provision for disabled students and those who experience difficulties in learning, *British Journal of Educational Studies,* 43, 398-411

Pritchard, D. G. (1963) *Education and the Handicapped 1760-1960,* London: Routledge and Kegan Paul

Radford, J. P. (1991) Sterilization versus segregation: control of the 'feeble-minded' 1900-1938, *Social Science Medicine*, 33, 449-458

Ray, L. J. (1982) Eugenics mental deficiency and fabian socialism between the wars, Bulletin of the Society for the *Social History of Medicine,* 30-32

Reilly, P. R. (1991) *The Surgical Solution: A History of Involuntary Sterilization in the United States,* John Hopkins University Press

Rose, N. (1985) *The Psychological Complex: Psychology, Politics and Society in England 1869-1939*, London: Routledge and Kegan Paul

Rosen, M. Clark, G. R. and Kivitz, M. S. (eds.) (1976) *The History of Mental Retardation: Collected Papers, Vols I and 2,* Baltimore: University Park Press

Ryan, J. and Thomas, F. (1987) *The Politics of Mental Handicap,* Free Association Books

Saunders, J. (1988) Quarantining the weak-minded: psychiatric definitions of degeneracy and the late-Victorian asylum, in W. F. Bynum, R. Porter, and M. Shepherd (eds.) *The Anatomy of Madness: Essays on the History of Psychiatry Vol. III,* London: Routledge

Scull, A. T. (1977) *Decarceration. Community Treatment and the Deviant: A Radical View,* New Jersey: Prentice Hall

Scull, A. T. (1979) *Museums of Madness: The Social Organisation of Insanity in 19th Century England,* London: Allen Lane

Scheerenberger, R. C. (1983) *A History of Mental Retardation,* Baltimore: Paul H. Brooks

Searle, G. R. (1976) *Eugenics and Politics in Britain 1900-1914*, Leyden: Science in History Series

Shennan, V. (1980) *Our Concern: The Story of the National Society for Mentally Handicapped Children,* London: Mencap

Simmons, H. G. (1978) Explaining social policy: The English Mental Deficiency Act of 1913, *Journal of Social History,* 11, 387-403

Stainton, T. (1991) Legacy of our caring predecessors, *Community Living,* (Oct) 14-15

Stainton, T. (1992) A terrible danger to the race, *Community Living,* (Jan) 18-20

Stainton, T. (1992) The seeds of change, *Community Living,* (Apr) 20-22

Stainton, T. (1992) Big talk, small steps, *Community Living,* (Jul) 16-17

Sutherland, G. (1984) *Ability Merit and Measurement,* Oxford: Clarendon Press

Taylor, P. (1994) Learning from experiences, *Soundtrack,* (Mar) 10-11

Thomas, D. J. (1969) A Guide to the Literature of Special Education

Thompson, M. (1984) *The Mad, the Bad and the Sad: Psychiatric Care in the Royal Edinburgh Asylum (Morningside) 1813-1894,* PhD thesis, Boston University

Thompson, P. (1988) *The Voice of the Past: Oral History (2nd ed.)* Oxford: Oxford University Press

Thompson, P. (1991) Oral history and the history of medicine: a review, *Social History of Medicine,* 4, 371-383

Thompson, P. and Perks, R. (1993) *An Introduction to the Use of Oral History in the History of Medicine,* London: National Sound Library Archive

Thomson, M. (1992) *The Problem of Mental Deficiency in England and Wales 1913-1946,* D.Phil thesis, University of Oxford

Thomson, M. (1992) Sterilization, segregation and community care, *History of Psychiatry,* 3, 473-498

Trent, J. W. (1994) *Inventing the Feeble Mind: A History of Mental Retardation in the United States,* Berkeley: University of California Press

Trombley, S. (1988) *The Right to Reproduce: A History of Coercive Sterilization*, London: Weidenfeld and Nicholson

Tyor, P. and Bell, L. (1984) *Caring for the Retarded in America: A History,* Westport: Greenwood Press

Unsworth, C. (1987) *The Politics of Mental Health Legislation,* Oxford: Clarendon Press

Vecoli, R. J. (1960) Sterilization: a progressive measure? *Wisconsin Magazine of History,* 43, 193-200

Walmsley, J. (1995) *Gender Caring and Learning Disability,* PhD thesis,

Walmsley, J. (1995) Life history interviews with people with learning disabilities, *Oral History,* 23, 71-77

Walter, R. D. (1956) What became of the degenerate? A brief history of a concept, *Journal of the History of Medicine,* 11, 422-429

Watson, S. (1994) Malingerers, the weak-minded criminal and the 'moral imbecile': how the English prison medical officer became an expert in mental deficiency 1880-1930, in M. Clark and C. Crawford (eds.) *Legal Medicine in History*, Cambridge: Cambridge University Press

Weiner, M. J. (1990) *Reconstructing the Criminal Culture, Law, and Policy in England, 1830-1914,* Cambridge: Cambridge University Press

Wolfensberger, W. (1975) *The Origin and Nature of Our Institutional Models,* Syracuse, N.Y: Human Policy Press

Woodhouse, J. (1982) Eugenics and the feeble-minded: the Parliamentary debates of 1912-1914, *History of Education,* 11, 127-137

Wright, D. and Digby, A. (eds.) (1996) *From Idiocy to Mental Deficiency: Historical Perspectives on People with Learning Disabilities,* London: Routledge

Yow, V. (1994) *Recording Oral History*, London: Sage

Zihini, L. (1989) *The History of the Relationship between the Concept and Treatment of People with Down's Syndrome in Britain and America from 1866 to 1967,* PhD thesis, University of London

Index

Families 86, 88, 92, 97-103, 131
  "problem families' 88, 131
Family Planning Association 131
Farleigh Hospital 114
Feeble-Minded 39-41, 68, 70-72, 113
Frome Workhouse 111, 114-115, 117, 120

Gender 99, 101, 103
'Grades' of Residents 39-41, 58-61
Guardianship 85, 96, 99, 103

Health Visitors Association 132
History
  interest in 2-6
  local 83, 84, 87, 88, 92, 103
  oral 2, 6-12, 35-45, 51, 83, 88, 89-91, 128
  uses of 12-13
Hospitals 84, 85, 86-88, 90-92, 102, 129
Hostels 88

Idiots 41, 109, 110, 111-112
Institutionalisation 38, 39
Institutions 11, 13, 36, 48-50, 52, 57, 62, 68, 98, 101, 108, 113, 116, 117, 121,
  certified 115, 116
  closure of 2-3
  network of 109, 114, 117
  regimes 24-29, 37, 38-43, 62
  types of 53-56
Imbeciles 41, 111, 112, 114
  Visiting Committee for 111
Immorality 41, 98, 99

Lancashire and Cheshire Society for the Permanent Care of the Feeble-Minded
66-71 *passim*
Lapage, C.P. 71
Learning Disabilities/Difficulties
  use of terms 14, note 1
Licence 97, 103
Little Plumstead Hospital 88
Local Authorities 84, 87, 91, 103
  records of 50
Local Policy 102, 103-104
Lunacy Act, 1890. 110

Mencap 3, 16, 88, 89, 90, 91
Mental After Care Association 132

Mental Defective (use of terms, 14, note 1, 15) see also 4, 39, 68, 70, 102, 103, 109, 110, 112-116 *passim*, 120, 121
Mental Deficiency 88, 108
Mental Deficiency Act, 1913. 36, 38, 39, 41, 52, 53, 63, 84, 96-97, 99, 100, 114-115
Mental Deficiency Committees 84, 86, 95-98, 102, 104, 114, 116, 117, 120, 131
Mental Health Act, 1959. 52
Metropolitan Society for Idiots and Imbeciles 48

National Association for Mental Health 131, 132
National Association for Mental Welfare 84, 97
National Health Service 4, 48, 49, 52, 73, note 1, 84
National Society for Lunacy Reform 131
Norah Fry Hospital 108, 114
Normalisation 17, 18, 19
Normansfield Hospital 57
Nurses 57-63

Occupation Centres (adult training centres) 85, 88, 91, 131
Oral History 2, 6-12, 35-45, 51, 83, 88, 89-91, 128

People First 3, 19, 32, 33
Photographs
  as sources 37, 65-74, 121, 131, 133
  films 129
  Iconographic Department 129
Poor Law Act, 1879. 110
Poor Law Institutions 108, 111, 115, 116, 120
Public Records Acts, 1958, 1967. 72, 76
Public Records Office 49
Punishments 28-29, 42-43

Reminiscence 91, 92
RESCARE 52
Rescue Homes 98
Retreat, The 129
Royal Albert Institution 57
Royal Commission on the Care and Control of the Feeble-Minded 49, 108, 112
  Medical Expert to 113
Royal Eastern Counties Institutions 47-64

Sandhill Park Colony 117, 119, 120
Sandlebridge Colony 65-74
Selwood Hospital 108, 114
Segregation, according to sex 24-25, 39-41, 62-63, 68
Shepton Mallet Workhouse 114-115, 116, 117, 120
Shuttleworth, G.E. 57, 71, 129
Somerset Association for Mental Welfare 119